THE EZEKIEL QUESTION: A SKEPTIC AT WORK!

"It all began with a telephone conversation between Long Island and Huntsville. Our son, Christoph, mentioned that he had just read a fascinating book about visits from outer space. Its title: *Chariots of the Gods?* Its author: a certain von Däniken.

"For me, an engineer who began his career in aircraft design in 1934, and who was working on large rockets and spacecraft, such books provide wonderful entertainment, and no more: they describe exciting events that occurred at times and in places that cannot be checked. So, when the 'Däniken' arrived, I read, smiled, grinned, and laughed—until I found the passage in which von Däniken writes about the prophet Ezekiel. Here were technical statements and claims right in the fields of my own professional knowledge! Suddenly it seemed very easy—I would take a *Bible* and would explain why a certain von Däniken was wrong. How sure I was!

"I soon lost my grin, became profoundly curious, and what followed was a wonderful experience, unusual in every respect, an undertaking which was done exclusively in my spare time, since NASA, my employer, is not engaged in such matters.

"Hardly ever was a total defeat so rewarding, so fascinating, and so delightful!"

JOSEF F. BLUMRICH

The Spaceships of Ezekiel

JOSEF F. BLUMRICH

BANTAM BOOKS · TORONTO · NEW YORK · LONDON

RLI: $\dfrac{\text{VLM 9 (VLR 9–10)}}{\text{IL 9-adult}}$

THE SPACESHIPS OF EZEKIEL
A Bantam Book | published February 1974

*Originally published in German by Econ Verlag GmbH
under the title
Da tat sich der Himmel auf
1st printing ... March 1973
2nd printing ... April 1973*

Published simultaneously in the United States and Canada

*Bantam Books are published by Bantam Books, Inc. Its trade-
mark, consisting of the words "Bantam Books" and the por-
trayal of a bantam, is registered in the United States Patent
Office and in other countries. Marca Registrada. Bantam
Books, Inc., 666 Fifth Avenue, New York, New York 10019.*

PRINTED IN THE UNITED STATES OF AMERICA

CONTENTS

FOREWORD

I wrote this book after reading *Chariots of the Gods* by Erich von Däniken.

I began to read von Däniken with the condescending attitude of someone who knows beforehand that the conclusions presented can by no means be correct. However, von Däniken quotes, among other things, passages from the Book of Ezekiel, whose vague technical information he thinks is a description of a spacecraft. With that he touches on a field very familiar to me, since I have spent the greater part of my professional life with design and analysis of aircraft and rockets. So I decided to use the statements of the prophet to refute von Däniken and to prove the fallacy of his allegations.

Seldom has a total defeat been so rewarding, so fascinating, and so delightful!

Huntsville, Alabama, November 1972
Josef F. Blumrich

1

THE SITUATION

THIS book is the result of a search. A search is like a question and as such provides as yet no clue to the relationship of the searcher to the object of his search. The person who asks must not necessarily believe in the existence of whatever he is inquiring about: he primarily looks for either a confirmation or a negation.

Genuine search requires objectivity. The latter cannot exist without mental flexibility, since none of us is objective by nature. We all have opinions, the roots of which are spread out far and often are hidden in darkness. To have an opinion is both our right and our duty. To change this opinion becomes an intellectual obligation if the opinion proves incompatible with the result of the search. Such a situation is a challenge that we cannot evade and therefore a conflict that becomes the touchstone of our objectivity and intellectual maturity.

The result of a search is not equally significant or convincing to everyone. The degree of intellectual conflict varies accordingly. The fervor of a controversy depends on the severity of such conflicts. But the deliberate application of objectivity softens the conflict and allows the controversy to become a discussion, a dialogue.

It may also lead to understanding!

Thus striving for objectivity, I am presenting engineering proof of the technical soundness and reality of the spaceships described by Ezekiel, as well as of the related events and procedures.

Lacking any applicable experience as he did, Ezekiel often had to resort to figurative descriptions to be able to report at all that he had seen. Such figurative description is confusing and mysterious so long as one knows nothing of the underlying reality. However, when we penetrate these pictures, we see immediately a surprisingly clear report, free of contradictions. One is then able to also recognize, so to speak, direct and uncoded parts of the report and to comprehend their significance.

It would appear that Ezekiel sensed the truth rather early. As his encounters with spaceships extend over a span of twenty years, we are in a fortunate position to deal with repeated observations of a specific type of space vehicle rather than an isolated event.

The prophet displays an extraordinary gift of observation in describing structure and functions of this type of spacecraft as well as the living beings and events immediately related to it.

Ezekiel begins his book with the description of the final phase of a spaceship's descent from a circular orbit to the earth and of its subsequent landing. This narrative is accompanied by a description of the main parts of the spacecraft. Remarkable is that in describing his last encounter with a spaceship, he explicitly stresses its apparent identity with the one he had seen twenty years earlier.

Ezekiel also speaks of the commanders of the spaceships; he hears them talk, he observes their movements; on one occasion he witnesses a peculiar event involving the participation of a ground crew summoned by the commander. He takes part himself in flights in these spaceships; two flights take him to temples whose location and significance are still unsolved mysteries.

The key to the clear understanding of Ezekiel's report lies in a very careful analysis of his description of the components of the spacecraft and of their function, carried out in the light of today's knowledge of spacecraft and rocket technology. This method proved successful very quickly. Further and increasingly detailed investigations and comparisons have shown that Ezekiel's descriptions are amazingly accurate. The amount and accuracy of detail reflected in his record lead to the conclusion that he must have possessed extraordinary gifts of observation and an almost photographic memory. This made it possible not only to develop a simple sketch, but also to express dimensions, weights, and capabilities in figures. Thus, for the first time, it became possible to free an ancient report on spaceships from its disguising pictures and to transpose it into the language of engineers. This breakthrough made it further possible to interpret occurrences which had seemed to have no real meaning.

The results obtained show us a space vehicle which beyond any doubt is not only technically feasible but in fact is very well designed to fulfill its functions and purpose. We are surprised to discover a technology that is in no way fantastic but even in its extreme aspects, lies almost within reach of our own capabilities of today, and which is therefore only slightly advanced beyond the present state of our technology. Moreover, the results indicate a spaceship operated in conjunction with a mother spacecraft orbiting the earth.

What remains fantastic is that such a spacecraft was a tangible reality more than 2500 years ago!

Of course, these results are in sharp contrast to text interpretations by many devout and learned men during all the past centuries. We have, however, to bear in mind the obvious fact that, throughout this long period of time, no man-made flying machines and rockets have existed. An interpretation of the text in this direction was therefore excluded in advance. By necessity, interpretations of Ezekiel's enigmatic statements had to be sought in the only possible direction, which was that of religion and particularly of mysticism. Therefore, nothing could be more wrong than to undervalue the endeavors of those men.

Besides, it must be emphasized that a technical interpretation of Ezekiel's writings has become possible only since December 1964 and this despite all the progress of the last decades. At that time, Roger A. Anderson, a leading engineer of NASA's Langley Research Center, published an article on structures technology (Reference 8) in which he described the shape of a spacecraft he had developed for entry into planetary atmospheres. This is the very shape we find in the central body of the spaceship. Without the knowledge of this fundamental possibility, a technical interpretation of the text would not be feasible even today.

The controversy on whether contacts with extraterrestrial civilizations is or is not possible is alive today throughout the world and involves various scientific and engineering disciplines. Despite wide discrepancies of views there are some points of general agreement. It is unanimously agreed that we can establish contact only with such civilizations (or they with us) as have either attained or surpassed our stage of development. Therefore we are justified in assuming that we are capable of at least some estimate of the effort required for such ventures both in technical and financial terms. The latter point is significant since we must assume that an extraterrestrial civilization too will have developed concepts of values and therefore will know financing problems. This notion, combined with the reality of the spaceships actually seen by the prophet, makes it appear unthinkable that their operation could have been concentrated on one single man. One is compelled to draw the inevitable conclusion that such missions must have encompassed a broader span in terms of their distribution in time and geographical locations. Evidence of such a scattering would provide a broad basis for the knowledge of extraterrestrial visits. Research toward this objective will hopefully become the joint goal of archaeologists, linguists, *and* engineers, working in close cooperation.

Of course the finding of tangible debris possibly resulting from crashes or crash landings could become highlights of such research work. Many would even regard the finding of such debris as a prerequisite for admitting the existence of spaceships in prehistoric or early historic periods. The similarity between this kind of skepticism and the "doubting Thomas" is quite limited, since in our case figures and technical know-how as well as literary and archaeological findings take the place of an act of faith. However, and beyond any personal attitudes, tangible findings would be of such decisive significance that a brief treatment of this question is appropriate.

For the time being, archaeology is the only source of relevant information. Its primary field of activity is in the areas of human settlements. On the other hand, as we know from our own experience, the chances of a crash or a crash landing in or close to a settlement are extremely low. But even in the event of such an unlikely occurrence the debris would have been very quickly removed and the damaged buildings restored. It is true that small pieces of metal from the body of the spaceship or possibly parts of some electronic equipment could be found in the soil, assuming favorable corrosion conditions. However, the probability of an archaeologist going to work with spade, hammer and brush on the exact spot of the crash is many times smaller than the chance of the crash itself. Accordingly, one can scarcely hope, for the time being, to find such traces of a crash within the limits of human settlements. However, truly scientific archaeology is still but a few decades old . . .

What archaeology did not find—simply because it practically had no chance to—is far more than compensated for by what it really brought to light: Very substantial material is available even in the field discussed here. Its sifting and exploitation is, however, outside the competence of archaeologists, it is in the field of engineering and requires highly qualified engineers whose structural knowledge will enable them to detect functional relationships.

In the field of literature the Book of Ezekiel is definite evidence—though of unusual nature—of the likelihood of further findings. But here again the task of evaluation falls within the competence of engineers.

In the previous paragraphs I have made repeated reference to the need for participation by engineers. This need becomes absolute for the assessment of structures or structural forms. Investigations and studies of this kind lie, so to speak, *within* the field of science. Science deals with questions of limits of knowledge. Matters lying within these limits become tasks of engineering. The engineer, and especially the design engineer, is the one who develops even the most advanced structures and who faces the task of thinking through and implementing the conditions and reasons that determine their shape. This is why he is the most competent person to deduce the purpose and the use of a structure from its outward appearance.

Another aspect of these studies concerns the idea that such visitors and their equipment—for fundamental reasons—would have to be and look different from us and from whatever we use. The tendency to attribute a priori to an extraterrestrial civilization fanciful, mysterious, or unfamiliar shapes and capabilities often overlooks the proposition that a resemblance is in fact much more probable than a substantial difference. We shall come back to this theme later.

Today any mention of extraterrestrial visits immediately brings up the question "Where from and how?" This is only natural since, in the final analysis, the answer to this dual question is of literally worldwide importance. But we have no answer. For the time being the problems it entails are too numerous and too large for us to resolve. This often leads to a conclusion which in its simplest form would be approximately tantamount to saying: "We do not know where they came from, so they can not have been here."

It is obviously impossible to overcome and to resolve this mountain of problems all at once. Therefore it appears to me that it would be far more appropriate to follow in this area a course regarded as self-evident in all other fields: to divide the total complex problem into smaller problems and questions.

Ezekiel points the way in this direction. He has described the presence of spacecraft so accurately that we can confirm the authenticity of his depiction by figures and with our knowledge of technology. Thanks to his key document we can begin to find confirming traces of evidence from other sources too. We should therefore amend the position as outlined above and say: "They were here, so they must have come here."

The changed psychological background reflected in this new formulation cannot fail to have an impact on the attitude toward the question "Where from and how?"

With regard to my own work I want to say that I have carried it out from the viewpoint of an engineer, out of technical curiosity, so to speak. My interest was primarily focused on those parts of the Book of Ezekiel that contain statements describing shapes and procedures relevant to my professional area of activity. These parts, incidentally, are almost without any exception clearly distinct from the prophetic content. Some non-technical conclusions were drawn from considerations embracing the overall contents, on the basis of the technical materials available.

The considerable reservations with which I began this study yielded to a very positive attitude as a consequence of the truly enormous prospects that became apparent when the application of well-established technical formulas and principles produced plausible results. The investigation included necessarily the consideration of possible improvements and developments insofar as they can be assessed today. Therefore, the conclusions give us not only the answer to the question "Is such a vehicle possible?" but also to its corollary: "How much higher developed was that historic technology than our own today?"

I would not have written this book had the answers I found seemed implausible or fantastic.

2

WHO WAS EZEKIEL?

SINCE we will analyze and evaluate Ezekiel's statements, his own person becomes the source for far-reaching conclusions. It is desirable to find out as much as possible about the kind, substance, and educational level of the personality that stands behind these reports. These characteristics contribute to the determination of the amount of trust to be accorded to the information. A report from a man who has never gone beyond the boundaries of his native community, his work, and his family has a weight different from that made by a man who must be described as educated and endowed with rich experience.

Direct information may be derived from his own reporting: The book begins in the year 593 or 592 B.C. Some five years earlier in 597, Ezekiel had been deported to Babylon with many other Jews by King Nebuchadnezzar. He lived in the community of Tel-Abib on the Chebar River (which was actually a canal) in Chaldea. Ezekiel was a priest. The fact that he was married is disclosed by the mention of the death of his wife four and a half years after the beginning of his prophecies. His father's name was Buzi.

Further deductions—even more relevant to our objective—may be made indirectly from the general political situation of his time and from certain passages in his writings. The fact, for example, that Ezekiel was among those deported indicates that his family had a certain social status, because the deportations of the year 597 B.C. involved the most influential part of the population.

Further, Tel-Abib was situated close to and south of Babylon. The assumption is therefore justified that Ezekiel had seen the great tower or at least had heard precise descriptions of that structure. It is also most probable that he had at least heard descriptions of the famed giant gate of the city as well as of the wide triumphal avenue leading toward it. Ezekiel knew the people of the country and had also doubtless seen enough of soldiers clad in their armor as well as the horse-drawn combat chariots.

He probably was about thirty years old. Therefore he must have reached the age of about fifty at the time of the last prophecy recorded in his book. He had been raised in Jerusalem, and as a result of his exile he became very familiar with two significant cultures. Moreover, the writings reveal that he was quite familiar with the cultural and trade situation in the whole of the Near East including Egypt. Nothing in his reports is primitive or simplistic.

The sum total of this information shows us a man of considerable experience who, as a member of an upper-class Jewish family, had enjoyed the benefit of a good upbringing and education.

It is not known when and where Ezekiel died, nor is it known where he was buried. His supposed though unconfirmed tomb is located near Al-Kifl, a settlement located a little less than twenty-five miles south of Babylon, according to the map "Lands of the Bible Today" (Reference 9).

3

WHAT DID EZEKIEL SEE?

ONCE we have penetrated all imagery, clarified and sifted what was dark, what is it that we can actually see and experience through and with Ezekiel?

The following descriptions of his experiences will be introduced by the relevant Biblical texts in order to give an impression of the kind of presentation involved. In the course of the subsequent analysis (section 5) I will have to revert necessarily to the same verses; nonetheless I feel that their contextual presentation at this point contributes to rounding off the overall picture. (Biblical texts as in References 3 and 5. See explanation on p. 51.)

THE BOOK OF THE PROPHET EZEKIEL

1:1. In the thirtieth year, in the fourth month, on the fifth day of the month, as I was among the exiles by the river Chebar, the heavens were opened, and I saw visions of God.

1:2. On the fifth day of the month (it was the fifth year of the exile of king Jehoiachim),

1:3. The word of the Lord came to Ezekiel the priest, the son of Buzi, in the land of the Chaldeans by the river Chebar; and the hand of the Lord was upon him there.

1:4. As I looked, behold, a stormy wind came out of

the north, and a great cloud, with brightness round about it, and fire flashing forth continually, and in the midst of the fire, as it were gleaming bronze.

1:5. And from the midst of it came the likeness of four living creatures. And this was their appearance: They had the form of men,

1:6. But each had four faces, and each of them had four wings.

1:7. Their legs were straight, and the soles of their feet were round; and they sparkled like burnished bronze.

1:8. Under their wings on their four sides they had human hands. And the four had their faces and their wings thus:

1:9. Their wings touched one another; they went every one straight forward, without turning as they went.

1:10. As for the likeness of their faces, each had the face of a man in front; the four had the face of a lion on the right side, the four had the face of a bull on the left side, and the four had the face of an eagle at the back.

1:11. And their faces and their wings were spread out above; each creature had two wings, each of which touched the wing of another, while two covered their bodies.

1:12. And each went straight forward; wherever the spirit would make them go, they went, without turning as they went.

1:13. In the midst of the living creatures there was something that looked like burning coals of fire, like torches moving to and fro among the living creatures; and the fire was bright, and out of the fire went forth lightning.

1:14. And the living creatures darted to and fro, like a flash of lightning,

1:15. Now as I looked at the living creatures, I saw a wheel upon the earth beside the living creatures, one for each of the four of them.

1:16. As for the appearance of the wheels and their construction: their appearance was like the gleam-

ing of a Tarsis stone; and the four had the same
likeness, their construction was as though one
wheel were within another.

1:17. When they went, they went in any of their four
directions without turning as they went.

1:18. The four wheels had rims; and their rims were
full of eyes round about.

1:19. And when the living creatures went, the wheels
went beside them; and when the living creatures
rose from the earth, the wheels rose.

1:20. Wherever the spirit would make them go, they
went, for the spirit made them go; and the wheels
rose along with them; for the spirit of the living
creatures was in the wheels.

1:21. When those went, these went; and when those
stood, these stood; and when those rose from the
earth, the wheels rose along with them; for the
spirit of the living creatures was in the wheels.

1:22. Over the heads of the living creatures there was
the likeness of a firmament, shining like rock crystal, spread out above their heads.

1:23. And under the firmament their wings were
stretched out straight, one toward another; and
each creature had two wings covering its body.

1:24. And when they went, I heard the sound of their
wings like the sound of many waters, like the thunder of the Almighty, a sound of tumult like the
sound of a host; when they stood still, they let
down their wings.

1:25. And there came a sound from above the firmament over their heads; when they stood still, they
let down their wings.

1:26. And above the firmament over their heads there
was the likeness of a throne, in appearance like
sapphire; and seated above the likeness of a throne
was a likeness as the appearance of a man upon
it above.

1:27. I saw as it were gleaming bronze, as the appearance of the fire round about enclosing him.
Upward from what had the appearance of his loins,
and downward from what had the appearance of

his loins, I saw as it were the appearance of fire, and there was brightness round about him.

1:28. Like the appearance of the bow that is in the cloud on the day of rain, so was the appearance of the brightness round about. Such was the appearance of the likeness of the glory of the Lord. And when I saw it, I fell upon my face, and I heard the voice of one that spoke.

What does Ezekiel describe?

His report begins without any introduction. He hurls the events of the first encounter at the reader with the same poignancy with which he himself had been confronted. The roar of the rocket engine ignited at that very moment explodes in the stillness and makes him look up. The flames of the engine are shooting from the center of a white cloud. Blinding light and a mighty roar come from there. The sky seems to burst open. The cloud allows a glimpse of four elongated shapes above which something as yet undefined is moving. At their lower end one can perceive straight legs and their round feet. For a moment Ezekiel has the impression that these shapes look like human beings. But then the clouds are dispelled, the blazing fire of the rocket engine suddenly vanishes: there can now be no doubt that those shapes have wings which are moving. Below these wings, arms are hanging downward alongside the body; above them Ezekiel discerns forms and shadows resembling faces. Similarity with human forms is certainly not complete but there is some approximation, and whatever Ezekiel sees must be living beings which now, quite close to him, are nearing the ground.

At all times we must remember that Ezekiel does not interpret what he sees, because he cannot interpret it. What he does is describe to the best of his ability the optical and acoustical impression, and in so doing he uses means which are available to him in view of this phenomenon. Looking at Figs. 1 and 2 in that context, it requires a bare minimum of imagination to recognize in this description the spacecraft in the last phase of its flight from the orbit around the earth. Fig. 3 is an ex-

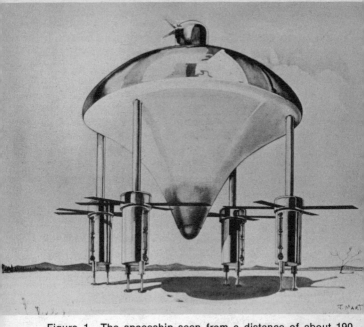

Figure 1   The spaceship seen from a distance of about 190 feet

ample of the depiction of the traditional interpretation.

The spacecraft began its flight to the earth with the separation from the mothership at an altitude of probably about 220 nautical miles. During the flight through the atmosphere, its speed was reduced by aerodynamic drag until eventually, at low altitudes, a brief firing of the rocket engine reduced the speed enough so that the spaceship could use its helicopters for the rest of the descent. This last phase of the flight, which begins with the brief firing of the rocket engine, was witnessed and described by Ezekiel.

Later he observes the spacecraft as it hovers a few feet above the ground in search of a suitable landing site. The brief bursts of the control rockets occur in a sequence seen as irregular by Ezekiel who construes them as lightning flickering in the space that separates the living beings. This diverts his attention from the fascinating beings to the area between them, and thus he now sees the radiator of the reactor glowing like smoldering coals.

The spacecraft has landed.

Wheels, which were housed in the lower portion of the helicopter units during the flight, have now been deployed. The straight legs with their round feet no longer touch the ground.

Wheels!

Figure 2   Helicopter unit seen from a distance of about 25 feet

Figure 3   An example of the traditional version

For the first time Ezekiel discovers in the bewildering phenomenon something with which he is familiar, something to which he can apply his experience. This is sufficient reason for him to observe them at length, to describe them now and later in a conspicuously prolonged fashion. Even twenty years later, they serve him again to confirm the spacecraft's identity. After taking a close look at them, he is puzzled again.

What kind of wheels are these!

Their color is a light greenish blue, and on each wheel he observes motions which he cannot comprehend, rotations unfamiliar to him from any of the wheels he knows. There is so much movement in every wheel that it seems to him that there is more than one wheel within a wheel. And then—he cannot understand how they move on the ground. The wheels he knows roll in one direction. Should this direction be changed, the whole wheel has to be turned to the new direction. Here he sees, however, that they can move in any direction from where they stand . . . without being turned! Ezekiel does not simply accept this as a fact, he checks his own observations by watching whether the living beings perhaps turn and in so doing turn the wheels. But he discovers no such movements in them.

Ezekiel knows only wheels that roll because the vehicle of which they are a part is being pushed or pulled. This everyday experience lets him assume that here too the wheels move along with the living beings. He cannot have any knowledge of wheel drives and therefore cannot realize that the relationships are reversed in the case of these wondrous wheels and that the living beings are the ones that are set in motion by the wheels!

Finally, wheels are unknown to him that have special provisions on their rims designed to increase their sliding resistance on the ground. These round protrusions on the rims required for a mobility in two directions look to him "like eyes."

Eventually the wheels come to a standstill and set Ezekiel free for other observations. It is only now that he raises his eyes above the wings of the living beings and sees the mighty dome that reaches out far and stretches in a huge arch above them. He notices that the wings no longer turn but that each two pairs of them are folded up and down until they touch the living beings.

Up to that moment, he had been hearing a very loud noise which he had attributed to the wings of the living beings. Now, however, he notices a decrease in the noise since the wings have stopped moving. He discovers also that the noise was not caused by the wings at all, but rather had its source behind the surface of the arch. Perhaps he senses that there is some connection. But for him there is no possibility of a breakthrough to certainty, because he cannot know anything about high-performance engines, about central power plants, and about the fact that their noise diminishes when they are switched from full power to idling.

Now Ezekiel looks above the rim of the arch and perceives an unreal, almost immaterial mixture of light and color in the midst of which he sees a man sitting on a throne. (In other versions he uses the word "Adam" in the text, which indeed means a "man.") Light and coloration of a transparent command capsule are optically much more impressive than its simple geometrical shape and therefore furnish a very plausible means for a description. The man whom he sees is the commander of the spaceship, and his seat has an unmistakable resemblance to a throne. Ezekiel is overcome by the enormity of what he sees and sinks to the ground as a sign of submission. He hears the commander's voice.

2:9. And when I looked, behold, a hand was stretched out to me, and lo, a written scroll was in it;

2:10. and he spread it before me; . . .

3:12. Then the spirit lifted me up, and as the glory of the Lord arose from its place, I heard behind me the sound of a great earthquake;

3:13. It was the sound of the wings of the living creatures as they touched one another, and the sound of the wheels beside them that sounded like a great earthquake.

3:14. The spirit lifted me up and took me away, and I went in bitterness in the heat of my spirit, the hand of the Lord being strong upon me;

3:15. And I came to the exiles at Tel-Abib, who dwelt by the river Chebar. And I sat there overwhelmed among them seven days.

3:22. And the hand of the Lord was there upon me; and he said to me: "Arise, go forth into the plain, and there I will speak to you."

3:23. So I arose and went forth into the plain; and lo, the glory of the Lord stood there, like the glory which I had seen by the river Chebar; and I fell on my face.

3:24. But the spirit entered into me, and set me upon my feet; and he spoke with me and said to me . . .

8:1. In the sixth year, in the sixth month, on the fifth day of the month, as I sat in my house, with the elders of Judah sitting before me, the hand of the Lord God fell there upon me.

8:2. Then I beheld, and lo, a form of what had the appearance of a man; below what appeared to be his loins it was like fire, and above his loins it was like the appearance of brightness, like gleaming bronze.

8:3. He put forth the form of a hand, and took me by a lock of my head; and the spirit lifted me up between earth and heaven, and brought me in visions of God to Jerusalem, to the entrance of the gateway of the inner court that faces north, where was the seat of the image of jealousy, which provokes to jealousy.

8:4. And behold, the glory of the God of Israel was there, like the vision that I saw in the plain.

The texts quoted above are a further example of Ezekiel's descriptive style.

Though Ezekiel was understandably excited during this first encounter, he was able nonetheless to separate reason from emotion for quite a long period of time and to observe and register objectively. But now he is completely overcome by the shock, he has no memory of the flight which lasts only a short while and which concludes the first encounter. He returns to his community, and it takes him a whole week to recover.

The high degree of attention devoted by Ezekiel to the appearance of the spaceship during the first encounter is not repeated. The wheels alone receive a renewed thorough treatment in the description of the third encounter. However, each time, he explicitly emphasizes the identity of the newly observed spaceship with those of earlier encounters.

The second encounter has no significance from a technical point of view. During the third encounter, however, a situation loaded with suspense is described, which by all appearances seems to have been caused by the spaceship. The very location of the action is most remarkable since the temple where it takes place is not identical with the Temple of Solomon, where it occurs according to the Bible.

The commander has taken Ezekiel on a flight and lands his spacecraft in the inner court of the temple. Immediately after the landing he summons a ground crew. Seven men come out of a gate and align themselves before the commander. They receive orders and leave.

The commander is standing in the court of the temple with Ezekiel, when one of the men returns and—in a military fashion—reports: "I have done as thou didst command me." This man is distinguished from the others by his clothes which look as though they were made of linen but which soon turn out to be a protective suit. All of them carry equipment unknown to Ezekiel. None of these men is notably different in body shape or movements from humans as they are known to him.

The action now focuses on the spaceship on which some necessary manipulations are carried out; they may even have been the reason for this landing. The commander, standing at the entrance of the temple building, orders the man to go to the spaceship and to take a position close to one of the helicopter units. The very short distance between that man and the glowing radiator of the reactor now makes the need for a protective suit understandable.

A mechanical arm picks a red-hot component from the interior of the body of the spaceship and passes it on to the man in the protective suit, who leaves at once carrying it with him.

By all appearances this was a critical procedure because the commander took good precautions, at least for himself: on the one hand he had taken his capsule from the spacecraft and brought it close to him by remote control, so that he could use it in case of an emergency for removing himself speedily to a safe place. On the other hand we learn that yet a second spaceship was in the vicinity. It could have picked up the commander in case of emergency.

However, the well-prepared procedure is carried out without incident. The commander flies in the capsule back to the spaceship and starts it immediately for a short "leap" into the outer court. Ezekiel is taken to him, he receives his instructions, then watches the takeoff and the flight of the spaceship by which he had arrived, and is afterward flown back to his community by the second spaceship. Incidentally, after recovering from the shock of his first flight, Ezekiel enjoys his ensuing flights as wonderful experiences.

A pause of some nineteen years follows. During this

period, Ezekiel makes no mention whatever of any new encounters with spaceships.

But one day the commander picks him up again for a flight and takes him to a temple located at great altitude. The planning of this undertaking is again made manifest by the presence of a man who awaits Ezekiel at the landing site. As in the third encounter, the body shape, the movements, and the speech of that man present no peculiarities that the careful observer Ezekiel would find worthy of mention. The garment, however, does attract his attention. Its surface which resembles bronze or gold reminds him of his first encounter with the commander, whose suit he had described because of its flamelike light effects.

The man who awaits him carries two implements that look to Ezekiel's eyes like a cord of flax and a measuring reed. He specifically stresses to Ezekiel that he was brought here in order to see everything; he enjoins him to remember well what he sees.

Ezekiel is led through a large temple compound which he describes with a wealth of detail. After some time the spaceship by which he came flies from its landing place in front of the temple building into the inner court. Ezekiel too is taken there by his escort who stands next to him while the commander gives instructions to the prophet.

Ezekiel's report is discontinued abruptly so that unfortunately we do not know the sequel and the end of this last reported encounter.

In this summary I have omitted details that are not necessary for the presentation of essential factual information, just as I have generally refrained from treating parts of the Ezekiel reports that are unrelated to the technical interpretation, that is, parts which we consider his prophecies. As a result the technical data becomes much clearer and the events become more visible in outline and in logical connection.

Now, however, I shall leave this mode of presentation and turn my attention to all available details. Their role will be to produce proof of the reality of Ezekiel's reports with the help of detailed analyses and step-by-step comparisons.

4

THE SPACECRAFT

IF we want proof of (a) the fact of Ezekiel's encounter with spacecraft and (b) the accuracy of the observations made on these occasions, it is necessary to familiarize ourselves sufficiently with the spacecraft as such. To this end it will be described in all its components in this section of our book. This description is entirely based on the results of the analyses which I have compiled for technically interested readers and for engineers in the Appendix of this book, together with basic information, assumptions, and conclusions.

For the sake of a clearer presentation, the structure and the function of the spacecraft will be discussed separately.

The structure

The spacecraft consists of three major systems:

The central main body.
The four helicopters that support the main body.
The capsule for the crew, which is located on the upper side of the main body.

Figs. 1, 2, and 4 show the general appearance of the spacecraft.

The main body

The shape resembles more a child's toy—the humming top—than a futuristic flying machine. However, as we will see, the choice of this shape is very ingenious and indicates judicious planning.

The primary reason for the shape is aerodynamic requirements. The flight from space through the air and to the earth begins with a velocity of some 21,300 miles per hour. For the landing on the surface of the earth this enormous speed must be reduced to zero. By far the greatest part of this braking can be achieved by aerodynamic means if the body has a high aerodynamic drag. The quasi-conical lower portion of the spacecraft is superbly suited to this objective. During descent the tip of the lower part of the spacecraft will therefore be oriented in the direction of the flight. Apart from small angles of attack, the spacecraft flies downward along its main vertical axis (Fig. 4). Reverse conditions apply to

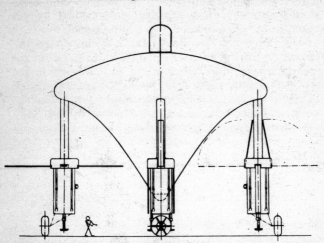

Figure 4   Engineering depiction of the spacecraft

the ascent: It occurs along the main vertical axis upward, and the upper side of the main body is exposed to the oncoming flow. While landing requires a high aerodynamic drag, the requirement for ascent is to keep it as low as possible. The aerodynamic drag of the upper side is mainly determined by the rounded profile of its outer regions; closer to the center its configuration is of lesser importance. For the concave profile of the underside, a round outer edge is also better than a sharp one. Thus, the requirements of both profiles are the same in their outer regions, allowing a smooth transition between two radically different aerodynamic bodies.

The concept of a configuration such as the quasiconical lower side we described was developed by Roger A. Anderson of the NASA Langley Research Center and published in December 1964 (Reference 8). This configuration was the result of an attempt to combine high aerodynamic drag and low structural weight. Both requirements were met in a brilliant fashion. The use of a concave profile to obtain a lightweight structure is a particularly elegant solution, because, with proper selection of this profile, only tensile stresses will occur in the surface structure which can therefore be made of thin sheet metal with a minimum of reinforcement.

The truly exceptional advantages of this design become fully evident especially in a vehicle like the one we are discussing. For flights within the atmosphere the spaceship requires four helicopters. The concave profile is ideally suited for this arrangement. The helicopter units can be located at the maximum distance from each other, which is very important for good flight characteristics. And it even becomes possible to fold the rotor blades upward within the arch of the concave body. With this arrangement, the main body is located *between* the helicopters. This solution reduces to a minimum the overall height of the spacecraft, and the total center of gravity is located as low as possible to provide the desired in-flight stability and landing properties.

At this time, no other spacecraft configuration is known which would reconcile the strongly divergent operational and structural requirements of this spacecraft. In this context we may think of the well-known shapes of the Mercury, Gemini, and Apollo capsules. It becomes immediately clear, however, that their configurations do not allow the inclusion of helicopters in the general layout.

In view of the mission that the spaceships described by Ezekiel obviously had, and given the level of technology apparently available to those unknown engineers, the configuration they chose was undeniably the key to realization. This is the reason for my earlier statement that a concrete technical interpretation of Ezekiel's report depends on Anderson's publication.

Having thus described and explained the outward shape of the main body, we shall now turn our attention to its installations. The main items involved are: the rocket engine (consisting of reactor, plug nozzle, and radiator), the propellant tank and the propellant, the central power plant for the helicopters, and additional units such as the environment control system and the propellant reliquefaction unit.

Just as the shape of the lower body was the key to our reconstruction, so the *reactor* is the key factor in the actual design. It is located in the lowest portion of the main body. This reactor is a reason why we are not yet able to build such a vehicle.

To understand that, we have to consider one of the most important characteristics in rocket calculations— the specific impulse I_{sp}. In its conventional definition this value indicates how many pounds of thrust are produced by an engine for each pound of propellant consumed per second. This definition means, among other things, that the less propellant consumed to produce a given thrust the higher will be the I_{sp} value. In the broadest sense, therefore, the specific impulse is an indication of the efficiency of a propulsion system. On the other hand the weight of the propellant accounts for by far the largest portion of the total weight, and a reduction of the amount of propellant is therefore of great importance. Herein lies, in a simplified presentation, the significance of the specific impulse.

It may happen that for a required flight program a given I_{sp} will result in weights and dimensions that exclude any feasible solution. In such a case it becomes necessary to turn to systems of a higher specific impulse. This is the situation we face with regard to Ezekiel's spaceships.

Our propulsion systems of today use pure oxygen or an oxidizer in combination with a fuel so as to produce high combustion temperatures. Depending on the propellants used, such systems today can reach I_{sp} values up to and above 400 seconds. (The simplified definition "second" is produced—according to the definition of I_{sp}— by dividing "pound" by "pound per second.") With the use of reactors this value reaches levels exceeding 900 sec because of their higher temperatures. However, the analysis in the Appendix to this book shows that Ezekiel's spaceship becomes a possibility only when I_{sp} values of 2000 sec or more are available! That is why a spaceship of this kind cannot be built today. Such values, however, are not as hopelessly beyond our grasp as comparisons with present figures seem to suggest. One may rather assume that it will become possible to design and build such propulsion systems within a few decades. The period of time that may be required to develop such systems depends on the successful solution of considerable technical difficulties which, in turn, would involve the investment of sizable financial resources. The development time is therefore contingent on the intensity of the effort. Consequently, the assumption may not be unjustified that such propulsion systems would perhaps be already in existence today if their development had been regarded as truly essential a number of years ago.

The reactor of the spacecraft is certainly not a system which lies—as far as we are concerned—in some dreamy and fantastic remote future; we are in fact quite close to it. When we say "close," we mean, in this case, close in terms of time. This assessment of closeness is based on the experience-supported expectation that a continuous intensive effort will bring about the technological success pursued. But in purely *technical* terms, we are still quite far from the goal.

These considerations on the comparison of our present knowledge with that alien technology are of much relevance to the evaluation of Ezekiel's observations.

They give us a new and much closer relationship to the Biblical spacecraft. The closeness of that technology strengthens the ground on which we stand in our evaluation.

We have recognized a recent development of our own times in the shape of the lower body of the spacecraft. The most recent progress in the study of materials enables us to expect with confidence considerable weight savings in future designs and to take this into account in the calculations involved. We are therefore well in a position to assess the feasibility of the spacecraft as shown in Figs. 1 and 4. Because we could build such a spaceship now . . . with the exception of the reactor. It is true that here and there we would have to cope with uncertainties with regard to the rest of the design. Appropriate development work would have to be planned and carried out. But all this is not new to us: Such situations are familiar to all those who are working in developing spacecraft or high-velocity aircraft.

On the outside, the *plug nozzle* is at approximately the same level as the reactor. In principle it is built like any other rocket engine; only the arrangement is different (Fig. 5).

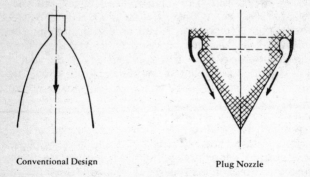

Conventional Design   Plug Nozzle

Figure 5   Schematics of rocket engines

The generally known engines have a circular cross section. The design of the plug nozzle is based on the concept of changing the circular cross section into a circular ring section. Such a design, while increasing the structural diameter of the engine, achieves a radical shortening of its structural length. If the type of vehicle is such as to allow the use of a plug nozzle, its structural height can be significantly reduced by eliminating the engine of conventional design. Moreover, since the diameter of the plug nozzle can be adjusted to that of the main structure, further structural simplification and weight savings will be achieved. The natural compatibility of the shape of the main body with the application of this advantageous principle is self-evident and one more indication of the correctness of its selection.

The *radiator* is located above the plug nozzle. An estimate of its size, that is, of the amount of surface it requires, is very uncertain because we have no real knowledge of either the reactor or of a possible additional cooling system. There is no doubt, however, that a large surface is needed. The radiator has accordingly a considerable upward extension and constitutes a part of the aerodynamic surface.

While the size is an unanswered question, fairly safe estimates can be made of the operational temperature of the radiator. Fundamental considerations of material properties let us expect temperatures on the order of 1000°–1300° centigrade (1800°–2300° F). This determination is important insofar as it indicates that the radiator glows when in operation.

As we have seen so far, the lower body of the spaceship—up to a probably relatively large distance from its "tip"—is subjected to high temperatures when the reactor and the nozzle are in operation. This area presents special difficulties with respect to both the selection of materials and the design. The same area experiences a roughly equivalent heat load during the braking phase of the flight through the atmosphere. At that time, however, the reactor is not operating, the surfaces in question are not heated by either the reactor or the plug nozzle and are therefore available for the thermal load of the braking. This dual function of one of the most complicated components of the vehicle is of great importance for its operation and efficiency. It is fascinating to observe such ingenious and judicious selection of the arrangement.

The propellant tank is located above and as close as possible to the reactor. The size of the intermediate space is determined by the structures that are required between the tank and the reactor: the main valve in the propellant line, the turbo-pump, and the radiation shield.

The need for these devices is easily understandable: The valve keeps the propellant in the tank as long as the reactor is not in operation, and it opens when the reactor is started. Then the turbo-pump delivers the propellant to the reactor in the quantity and under the pressure required. The radiation shield protects the crew in the capsule from the harmful radiation of the reactor. The crew spends most of its time in the capsule; the radiation dose in that direction must therefore be kept at as low a level as possible. Although the propellant in the tank does provide some shielding, most of the radiation must be blocked by a special shield. The radiation shield must be large enough to prevent the capsule from being exposed to the radiation coming from the reactor. To use an image, the reactor must not be able to "see" the capsule. This concept explains why the lateral extension of the thickest portion of the shield can be relatively small. The shielding of the other sides of the reactor can be made thinner and lighter because there is rarely anybody in that direction and if so for only a short time.

The propellant tank occupies most of the volume of the spacecraft. It begins, as already mentioned, somewhat above the reactor and extends upward, reaching beyond the region of the maximum diameter of the main body. Its outline essentially follows the concave outside profile (Fig. 16, Appendix). Some space is required between the vehicle surface and the tank to provide room for structural members, pipes, cables, and insulating material. The upper side of the tank has a large diameter, which would make a bulkhead with the customarily elliptical cross section uneconomical. We can safely assume that a special design was used. Designs of that kind are mentioned in the technical Appendix to this book.

Liquid hydrogen, which has a boiling point of about −253° C (−442.9° F), is used as propellant. Already today, insulation systems are available that can maintain such an extremely low temperature; and work for their improvement is being continued. Instead of liquid hydrogen the tank may contain a mixture of liquid and frozen hydrogen roughly comparable to what we commonly describe as slushy snow.

The last of the essential systems housed in the inside of the main body is the *central power plant* for the helicopter units. In its study we encounter yet another elegant solution in the design of the spaceship: one and the same energy source supplies two different users. The helicopters and the rocket engine are never in full operation simultaneously, and the reactor's energy can therefore be used to power either of the two systems as required.

The actual principle of the central power plant cannot be closely defined. Yet it is doubtlessly based on the transformation of the reactor's thermal energy into electric energy which, in turn, is converted into mechanical motion of the rotors.

In view of the weight estimates that follow later, an installation will be assumed that consists of a turbogenerator, electric motors, and transmission gears. The direct transformation of heat into electricity involves heavy equipment at today's state of the art; it may be expected, however, that this transformation will lead, after a sufficiently long period of development, to solutions that are more advantageous in terms of weight. For our purposes it is therefore preferable to consider the conventional system because it results in heavier weights and therefore increases the reliability of the weight estimates.

The assumed plant works as follows: The thermal energy of the reactor drives the turbine by evaporation of a not closely defined medium. The generator coupled to it produces the electric energy, which is transmitted by cables to electric motors, which drive the gears of the helicopters. The vapor is condensed after it leaves the turbine; the liquid medium thus regained is pumped into a container from where it can then be recycled. For the purpose of condensation a radiator may be considered that could be built into the upper surface of the spaceship, or, else, use can be made of the low temperature of hydrogen. In the latter case the reliquefaction unit, which is probably provided anyway, would have to be laid out accordingly.

Production of energy, and condensation, occur in closed cycles: Aside from minor loss due to leakage, neither the medium driving the turbine, *nor* hydrogen, is lost. This conclusion is of far-reaching significance since it shows us that the spaceship can fly in the atmosphere of the earth for unlimited lengths of time.

The helicopters

The most remarkable characteristic of these systems that are so important for the mission of the spaceship is the total lack of any unusual features: There is nothing in their entire layout that would be outside of our present knowledge and capabilities.

The arrangement of the rotor plane relative to the main body requires a columnlike structure between the connecting point on the outer rim of the main body and the helicopter as such (Figs. 1 and 4). The four helicopter units also turn out to be the natural elements for supporting the spacecraft on the ground. However, the landing legs and wheels needed for this purpose are at a considerable distance from the rotor plane. Accordingly, another supporting structure must exist below that plane, and the landing gear will be attached to its lower end. This supporting structure can be used advantageously for the attachment of the control rockets and to house their propellant containers. Since the shape of the latter is either cylindrical or spherical, the form appearing on Figs. 1, 2, and 4 emerges as a natural consequence. Moreover, there is room in the lower area of that cylindrical structure for the retractable wheel. For reasons explained later, the control rockets were placed on the side of the cylinder that faces the main body. Finally, the mechanical arms operated by remote control are also installed on the outer side of the cylinder. With their aid, one can carry out manipulations that may be required either on the spacecraft itself or with objects on the ground.

The *rotor* consists of four blades, which can be folded upward and downward in pairs when they are at rest. This blade arrangement is not complicated in principle but seems nonetheless peculiar; it raises therefore the question of its technical reasons.

The answer is partly supplied by the position of the helicopters during the braking phase, which will be discussed later: The rotor blades and especially those that are extended outward would be exposed to excessive aerodynamic loads (Fig. 11). There is therefore a definite reason for folding the blades, but it does not yet provide an explanation for the folding pattern in two opposite directions. The solution becomes understandable if one considers the rotors after the landing. As long as they are in their operating position, but not actually turning, one or two blades of each rotor are very close to the radiator. The latter, however, is still at its full operating temperature and the blades are necessarily exposed to its considerable heat radiation. Even with the use of appropriate materials, deformation of the blades could not be avoided and the rotor would become unusable at least temporarily. To avoid such problems, the blades must be removed from the proximity of the radiator; this is possible only by swinging them away or by folding them respectively. However, if all four blades were to hang downward, one blade would still be exposed to the heat of the radiator over its full length and width (blade no. 1 of Fig. 6). The two neighboring blades offer the smallest possible surface to the heat radiation (nos. 2 and 3 of Fig. 6); they are in the most favorable position attainable in this area. The unfavorable position of rotor blade no. 1 (Fig. 6) can be avoided, however, if it is folded upward instead of downward. Such a position moves the blade to the greatest possible distance from the radiator. An additional reduction of the heat input results from the fact that this blade is no

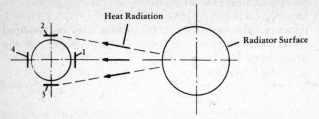

Figure 6 Heat input on rotor blades

longer positioned directly opposite the radiator. The folding of rotor blades in pairs therefore reduces to the barest unavoidable minimum the heat input and the related problems of blade distortion and material selection. This great advantage is no doubt the reason for the adopted arrangement.

When the rotor is in operation, however, all four blades do come close to the glowing surface with every revolution, but they are exposed to the heat for only a short time and are continuously cooled by the flow of air. From this results after a short time a stationary condition of only slightly increased temperature. This condition may be taken into account—if at all necessary —in the blade analysis, the design, and the materials selection. The cylindrical body of the helicopter is eventually fully exposed to the heat input over part of its surface; but it can be adequately protected by using appropriate materials and a suitable design.

As in all such structures, the great difference in the number of revolutions between the rotor and the drive motor requires the use of a reduction gear. In our contemporary designs, engine and gears are located below the rotor. In the vehicle we are discussing, however, the rotors are driven from above and consequently the gear is located above the rotor plane.

For aerodynamic reasons and also for protection against heat and dirt, the gear is surrounded by a fairing. The latter necessarily has a somewhat irregular shape since it must follow the outline of the gear; moreover, it requires small cutouts for the rods and levers of the blade controls. In addition, the fairing must have two deep cutouts for each of the two blades that fold upward. Such details have no technical significance by themselves. But we shall see in the next section of the book what significance they can assume for someone who—like Ezekiel—has no technical knowledge of what he sees.

So far only *one* rotor plane has been mentioned. It is possible, however, that the blades were in fact rotating in pairs at two levels, one above the other. This variation depends on the manner and method of equalization of the driving torque of the rotors. This has no influence on configuration and fundamental feasibility of the vehicle and will therefore not be further discussed.

The *control rockets* are used to perform small attitude corrections or course corrections in flight. The principle of their arrangement is shown in Fig. 7.

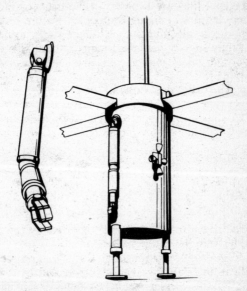

Figure 7   Mechanical arm and control rockets

Usually the control rockets are fired only briefly and they produce relatively small amounts of thrust. They are, in a way, the equivalent of the rudder of an aircraft or a ship. Depending on how many such small rockets are fired in short blasts, the vehicle can be rotated, tilted, or translated. An example from our own times: Anyone who has had a chance to watch the U.S. Apollo program on film or television will certainly recall the flashing of the control rockets as the module, coming up from the moon, was approaching the command capsule.

Two to four *mechanical arms,* operated by remote control, are fastened on the outside immediately below the rotor; when not in operation they hang downward. Each of these arms consists of a forearm and an upper arm, has an elbow, a wrist, and a hand. To extend the reach, the forearm and upper arm may be designed as telescoping members, which would give the mechanism roughly the appearance shown in Fig. 7. Near the shoulder and the wrist television "eyes" are probably installed to observe position and movements of the hand. Remote operation and control of the mechanical arms are performed from the command capsule. Even today, arms of this or similar types are already well-established technical products. Large-size versions of such arms are being investigated under the U.S. Shuttle Program. Figs. to the plane. Tread such as used in heavy tractor tires 8a and 8b show the shape of such a "hand."

Each *landing leg* consists of a simple straight shock absorber, which works in a telescopic fashion under load, and of a round disklike foot. The disk's purpose is to distribute the ground pressure over a surface large enough to prevent it from sinking into the ground. The underside of the foot usually has a convex shape to permit sliding, which may become necessary, for example, in case of a crosswind landing.

It may be of interest to mention here that it was the accurate description of these feet that motivated me to investigate Ezekiel's report more closely. Ezekiel says:

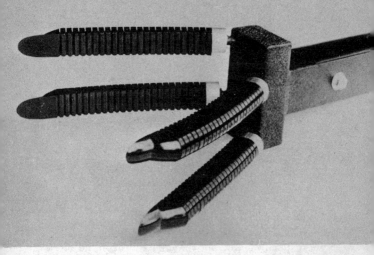

Figures 8a, 8b　Mechanical hand. We see here an excellent example of the similarity between technically highly developed structures and "natural" shapes serving the same purpose

1:7. Their legs were straight, and the soles of their feet were round; and they sparkled like burnished bronze.

Since I was involved myself in the design and testing of such "feet" years ago, Ezekiel's words made immediate sense to me.

The *wheels* allow rolling movement in any direction, without need for turning. This complex requirement can be met in a surprisingly simple manner.

Let us imagine the inner tube of an automobile tire (see the schematic movements in Fig. 9). It rolls, as we

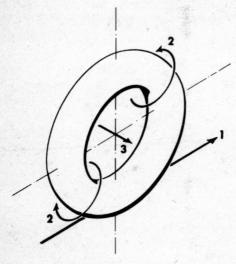

Figure 9   The principle of achieving wheel movement in any direction

know, in the direction of arrow 1. If, however, we twist that tube in itself—as indicated by arrows 2—then it will move along arrow 3, at a right angle to its customary rolling direction. An appropriate combination of the two directions of rotation will let the inner tube roll along any desired direction. With that, the problem is solved in principle. The simplest design resulting from the application of that principle is shown in Fig. 10. We see the "tire" divided into a number of barrel-shaped segments that are connected to the hub of the wheel by means of spokes. Both directions of rolling are achieved by the rotation of the wheel around its hub on the one hand and by the rotation of the segments around their own axes on the other.

Ezekiel has devoted special attention to the description of the wheels. The texts have often been misinterpreted. For this reason the technical Appendix to this book includes a detailed investigation of the wheel. At this point, therefore, it only remains for us to investigate the meaning of the repeatedly mentioned "eyes."

Fig. 10 shows the barrel-shaped segments as having a

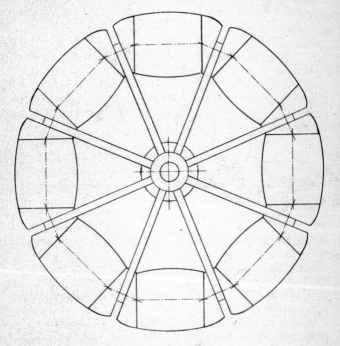

Figure 10   Structural layout of a wheel

smooth surface, which would result in a minimum of friction between wheel and ground. To increase friction, or sliding resistance, it is necessary to provide a profile. Resistance to slipping, however, is needed in two directions: in the plane of the wheel and perpendicular to the plane. Tread such as is used in heavy tractor tires or caterpillars would not be useful, because it would transmit the driving force only in the plane of the wheel. The simplest and most efficient solution is short protrusions that—similarly to the so-called sheepsfoot rollers used in road construction—are distributed over the surface of the segments. "Sheepsfoot," incidentally, is yet another example of how even now we still resort to figurative talk in identifying a modern device.

The short protrusions must be slightly conical—like the half-retracted eyes of a snail. To facilitate penetration into the ground they may be hollow: They would then have dark openings on their free ends. Seen from some distance, such dark openings can be legitimately compared to "eyes."

It should be further mentioned that the solution and design I developed for the wheel were found to meet patent requirements; a patent is now pending at the U.S. Patent Office.

With regard to the complete *helicopter units* another consideration is necessary. The desired aerodynamic braking effect of the lower part of the main body requires that it must be exposed to a free air flow. The proximity of the helicopters would destroy such an effect. Moreover, the helicopters would be exposed to aerodynamic loads and temperatures that would make their design extremely difficult. In their working position the helicopters are therefore incompatible with the braking phase and must be removed for its duration. But even this seemingly very demanding requirement can be met with astonishing ease.

As we have seen, the helicopters are attached to the main body close to its maximum diameter. Therefore, they can be rotated upward with relative ease, so that they assume the position depicted in Fig. 11. This is what the spaceship looks like at its entry into the earth's atmosphere. (For the sake of clarity I have not shown, in Fig. 11, the helicopters in the middle plane.) From

the point of view of aerodynamics the helicopters are
behind the main body in this position, the braking potential of which is thus fully effective. The structural design
of supports and mechanisms required to achieve this repositioning of the helicopters offers no basic difficulties.

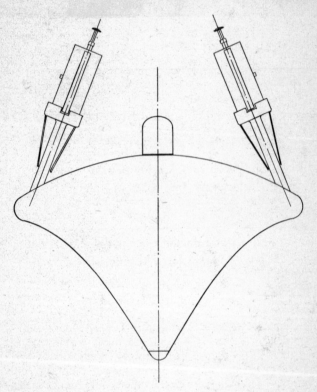

Figure 11   The spacecraft at entry into the atmosphere

This dual position of the helicopters has an interesting
consequence concerning the control rockets. When the
helicopters are down, that is, in their working position,
one would be tempted to attach the control rockets to
their outer side which is not facing the main body. But
then, in the upper position, they would come quite close

to the command capsule. When they operate in vacuum, the jet expands almost perpendicular to the axis of the nozzle, which could create a hazard for the command capsule. This alone could be reason enough to locate the control rockets on the opposite side. There is, however, one more important aspect that must be considered: The selected layout makes it possible to place the control rockets on the helicopters in such a way that they have, in both end positions of the helicopters, equal distance from the overall center of gravity of the spacecraft. That gives the commander the feeling of an unchanged "control response" when he fires these small nozzles, which is a considerable advantage from his point of view. The reversion of electrical signals, which is also necessary, can be made without much difficulty. The control rockets can of course also be operated while the helicopters are being repositioned.

The layout selected for the control rockets thus allows the use of one and the same control system during all phases of the flight. The simplicity, safety, and efficiency of this solution are evident.

The command capsule

The capsule is located at the center of the upper part of the main body and therefore at the uppermost point of the spaceship (Fig. 4). It consists of a cylindrical portion about 6½ feet in diameter and its upper part is convex like the bulkhead of a pressure vessel. This external shell is made of a glasslike transparent synthetic material. A sealed hatch through which the crew can leave the capsule is located in the curved upper portion. In the floor of the capsule a similar hatch provides access to the interior of the spaceship.

The capsule can be released and separated from its supporting structure. It can then leave the spaceship under its own power and later return to it. This procedure can be initiated and operated both directly and by remote control. Power for such flights is supplied by cold-gas rockets. This may sound fantastic, but it should be pointed out that such capabilities do not include elements that are not—at least on a smaller scale—available today.

Because of this independent flight capability, the capsule is supplied only with the necessary minimum of equipment. Most of the equipment is stored underneath in the spaceship; all installations of the capsule are automatically connected to it as long as the capsule remains attached to the vehicle, that is, as long as the capsule does not fly by itself.

The interior of the capsule thus contains only the two or three seats for the crew, the control equipment, the instrument panel, and the communication equipment. Normally, air supply is provided by the main unit, and small air supply units are provided only for use in case of an emergency.

With the exception of the seats, all other installations take very little room. Hence, visibility is excellent, which makes it also possible to clearly see the interior of the capsule from the outside!

The commander

Without any other identification Ezekiel always describes the commander of the spaceship simply as a "man." Despite his ability to observe and describe in great detail it seems that he did not see anything noteworthy. It can therefore be assumed that the commander looked like a human being and was not different from the average man of that time in size or shape of his body. The suit of the commander did impress Ezekiel, however—it had a surface resembling gold or brass. From our own work today we know that this indicates the intention of providing insulation against too high temperatures.

The commander is equipped with a device with which he can fly by himself. This capability is significant in several phases of his trip: after the landing of the spaceship the commander can use it to fly to the ground through the upper hatch. He will also use the same device to leap over obstacles on the ground or to avoid dangerous situations; he can also use it to fly back to his capsule at any time. In an unaccelerated flight outside the atmosphere the same device becomes important for inspecting and correcting small damages on the outside of the spacecraft.

For docking to the mothership, the capsule is probably taken into an air lock through which the commander can enter the mothership. His small propulsive device, in addition to being useful on the ground, becomes an absolute necessity if for some reason normal docking should be impossible. In such an emergency the commander will leave the capsule through the upper hatch and fly over to the mothership. Naturally, during all operations carried out in vacuum, he must wear his space suit. However, this is no obstacle to the functioning of the propulsive device.

It is necessary to stress here that the described capabilities of the device are neither exaggerated nor unrealistic. Propulsive devices of this kind were developed and tested for terrestrial use more than ten years ago. Fig. 12 shows a flight with such a device and is convincing evidence of the practical applicability of such systems. We know also of the experimental use of much smaller units in spaceflights performed to date. Of course, our designs of today represent very early stages, and there is no doubt that it will be possible to develop small devices of high quality that will far surpass contemporary models both in performance and in practical applicability.

In addition, whenever the commander leaves the capsule, he is doubtlessly equipped with a small communication unit. With an additional remote-control unit he can separate the capsule from the spacecraft and maneuver it in any direction.

The function

Starting point: orbit around the earth

Both the layout of the spacecraft as well as the analyses provide a sure indication that it was designed to serve as a shuttle between a mothership and the surface

of the earth. The mothership is in orbit around the earth and is both the starting point and the destination of all the spaceship's flights. We shall not put forward any considerations regarding the mothership and its origin. As already stated, my attitude results from the need to first solve *one* partial problem: to investigate the spacecraft as thoroughly as possible and to substantiate it through the knowledge acquired. We can turn to other problems only after we have fulfilled this task.

Regardless of where that undefined mothership may have come from, it must, upon arrival in the proximity of the earth, reduce its speed in order to be able to get into an orbit around the earth and stay in it. The closer its orbit is to the earth, the more speed it has to sacrifice. A correspondingly larger increase of speed is required when it begins its flight home.

Any change of speed—be it acceleration or deceleration—requires the thrust of the rocket engine. This means that propellant will be consumed. The smaller the differences in speed, the less propellant will be used. Therefore, an orbit of an altitude as high as possible is desirable for the mothership.

The very opposite applies to the small spacecraft: since it provides shuttle traffic to the earth, it requires more propellant for its flight the higher the orbit of the mothership. The longer the trip, the larger the spacecraft must be. If all the operating conditions are known, the optimal height of the mothership's orbit can be calculated. Theoretically, such optimum altitude can be any value above 150–200 kilometers (80–110 nautical miles).

These theoretical possibilities are, however, limited by the necessity of taking the Van Allen radiation belt into account. In our case its south Atlantic anomaly is of importance: Here the zone of increased intensity comes as close as approximately 350 kilometers (190 nautical miles) to the surface of the sea. We know today that flights through this radiation area are tolerated by the human body.

Figure 12   Flight with a one-man propulsion unit

Since we have no clues for an assessment of the optimum altitude, the assumption may be justified that the orbit of the mothership was some 350–400 kilometers (190–220 nautical miles) above the surface of the earth.

The flight to earth

The mothership circles around the earth with a speed of almost 34,000 kilometers per hour (21,300 mph).

The smaller spacecraft that separates from it for its flight to the earth begins its descent with the same rate of speed. At the end of the flight its speed relative to the landing point must be reduced to zero. We are therefore confronted with a braking action of huge magnitude.

For the largest part the braking force required is produced by the aerodynamic drag of the vehicle. This fact illustrates the significance of the shape of the lower body of the spacecraft.

Two aspects must be considered in connection with the braking process: the heat generated by air friction, and the magnitude of the deceleration. The heat is subject to limitation mainly by the properties of materials available for the heat shield. The magnitude of the deceleration has a direct impact on the crew and must be kept within limits they can bear without damage to their health.

The entry trajectory can be calculated on the basis of this twofold limitation.

Despite its high aerodynamic drag, toward the end of its journey to the earth the spacecraft is still falling with a speed exceeding 200 kilometers per hour (125 mph). The rocket engine is used to reduce this residual speed to zero, which is achieved in a short time. Of course, the spacecraft could land directly on the earth and later take off again by using its rocket engine only. But because of its mission, which we will investigate later, it must have the capability to cut off the rocket engine earlier. This is the reason for the presence of helicopters which seems somewhat surprising at first glance: If the rocket engine must be cut off before the completion of the descent, the flight can only be completed by aerodynamic means, that is, by means of the helicopters.

As we have seen, the helicopters must be in their upper position for aerodynamic reasons so long as the descent velocity is high. Conceivably, they could be rotated into their working position relatively early, that is, soon after the sink speed has dropped into the subsonic range. The rotors would then first work windmill fashion, and a slow increase of the angle of attack of the rotor blades would later reduce the sink speed. Obviously, however, the repositioning of the helicopters at such high velocities would be risky for stability reasons; in addition, the high blade loads would result in high helicopter weights.

On the other hand, the speed is greatly reduced anyway by the aerodynamic braking. It is better, therefore, to leave the helicopters in their upper position as long as possible and to start the rocket engine as late as possible. The engine thrust will entirely or almost entirely reduce the sink speed to zero, and the deployment of the helicopters can then be done while the craft is momentarily hovering or at a very low rate of descent. With that, all risks are avoided.

For the spin-up of the rotors some residual speed can be used or a desired rate of speed can be achieved by reducing the engine thrust. After the rotors have reached their normal speed of rotation, the main engine is cut off.

With this operation the spaceflight as such is over. During the next and last phase the spacecraft operates as a helicopter. Taking into account that reserves are certainly desirable should complications arise, it may be assumed that the helicopter flight would normally begin at an altitude of some 3000 feet above ground.

In most cases the commander will have to look for spots suitable to set down the landing legs before he can land the spacecraft. To that end he will keep the vehicle hovering for some time and will move it horizontally in various directions. He can carry out these maneuvers by using either the helicopters or the control rockets. Because of the slower and less precise reaction of the helicopters, the commander will probably prefer to use the control rockets. Since a continuous observation of the terrain is carried out, the spaceship moves very slowly. Therefore, compared to its great mass, its aerodynamic drag is very low and it moves practically without friction. Any movement resulting from a brief firing of control rockets can therefore be stopped only if other control rockets are fired in the opposite direction. This applies to horizontal movement, to tilting around two axes, and to a rotation about its vertical centerline. To an observer the control rockets will appear to flicker in an irregular manner, giving the impression of a very lively and manifold activity.

Finally, the commander sets the spaceship down on a suitable site. The flight to earth has ended.

If, for any reason, the location of the spacecraft must be changed, this can be done with the help of the wheels. For this purpose, they are deployed from the lower portion of the helicopters and set on the ground. By means of a suitable structural layout the landing legs can be raised easily from the ground, which makes a rolling motion possible. With the aid of the wheels the spacecraft can be moved slowly on the ground. The wheels also allow the commander to bring the spaceship much more precisely to a given spot than could ever be done by the helicopters or the control rockets.

The reactor is shut down upon completion of these maneuvers. Its temperature falls so slowly however that the radiator must remain in operation for some time. We have seen in the technical description that this condition constitutes one of the two reasons for folding the rotor blades.

Terrestrial flights

The helicopters are used for flights from one point on the surface of the earth to another. After the reactor reaches its full power, the rotor blades are deployed from their folded to their working position for the start and the rotor will be brought to its full speed of rotation.

During takeoff the total power requirement of the four

helicopters is about 70,000 horsepower. The noise produced by the rotors and the power plant is correspondingly high. Since, as has already been explained, there is no limitation to the flight duration, distances of any length can be covered.

The return flight

The start for the return flight into orbit and to the mothership can occur either directly with the aid of the rocket engine or it can begin with the helicopters. In our investigation of the spaceship's mission we shall discuss the considerations that determine the choice of the liftoff method.

If the rocket engine is used, the ascent is continuous. The helicopters remain inactive, their wings folded. Control rockets will be used for the final course corrections and for the docking to the mothership. For this kind of return flight the helicopters are not needed.

This fact allows an interesting conclusion: In emergency they can be left behind! Emergencies can arise from gear damage or from damage to one or several rotor blades. A loss of liquid hydrogen through damaged insulation or a breakdown of the reliquefaction unit also will cause acute emergency conditions. The separation and jettisoning of the helicopters from their points of attachment can be provided for by suitable structural arrangements. Should the helicopters be left behind, a considerable decrease in the total weight would ensue which would be most welcome in case of emergency. The loss of control rockets is doubtless unpleasant, but it can be partly offset by proper control of the engine thrust and partly also by rescue operations undertaken from the mothership.

A start by helicopters begins in the manner familiar to us today. The transition from this mode of ascent to the rocket flight takes place—as during the descent—at an adequate distance from the ground, that is, at an altitude of 3000 feet or more. This transition from one mode of ascent to another is somewhat critical because it takes a few seconds before the rocket engine develops its full thrust; this means that for a short moment the reactor has to supply power to both systems. Within this interval of time the lifting capacity of the helicopters can be brought down to zero, however, so that at least a hovering condition can be maintained through precise coordination. To avoid unnecessary drag and blade loads, the rotor blades are folded immediately afterward.

The rest of the flight is performed as a regular rocket flight.

Summary

The main features of the spaceship reveal to us a vehicle of a surprisingly sophisticated design. We recognize the aerodynamic and weight advantages inherent in the striking shape of the main body; we see how well suited it is for the addition of helicopters. The helicopters themselves are distinguished by such features as folding wings, ability to change their position, and astute layout of the control rockets. The dual use of the reactor is impressive. So is the advantageous layout of plug nozzle and radiator, and so are finally the various possibilities for landing and takeoff as well as the significant capability of undertaking unlimited terrestrial flights.

All these properties fit together without any contradiction or unsolved questions: they are unmistakable indications of very able and sophisticated planning and design.

5

BIBLE TEXT AND
SPACE TECHNOLOGY

THE knowledge we have of the structure and the functions of the spacecraft makes it now possible to view and to interpret the Biblical text in a new light. The details and conclusions of such an analysis give this chapter of the book the character of an entirely new Bible commentary. In accordance with the investigations undertaken, this commentary applies only to those parts of the text that are of interest with regard to the spaceship, its commander, the ground crews, and the events involved.

References 1–7 on page 175, Bibles and Bible Commentary, have been used as sources.

Every translation has its peculiarities. It is therefore necessary for a commentary of the kind presented here to select one as a main reference and to discuss deviations from other translations if and where they occur. Since the original version of this book was written in German, a direct replacement of the German Biblical text used there (Reference 5) by an English version was not feasible. Reference 3 was therefore used, but adapted to reflect the essentials of the German translation. That assures a meaningful connection between individual quotations and comments; it also allows, with the few exceptions of the adaptations, the use of an established Bible text in the English language.

All the translations and commentaries of the Bible used in this work are commercially available. I have chosen translations that not only cover a span of some 150 years, but also come from geographically and theologically widely differing quarters.

Initially I considered inviting the cooperation of an expert in ancient languages. However, I soon gave up this idea for two reasons: (1) Text differences as such, insofar as they are of linguistic origin, already *are* different interpretations by experts. The involvement of yet another expert would merely have added one more opinion, without any prospect of arriving at a final decision. (2) There are no fundamental or essential differences among these versions. All describe—and one could rightfully say, "naturally"—the same events and the same physical structures.

As the work progressed, this decision was proved correct again and again. In most cases the differences in the text could be traced back to word choices by translators and thus clarified and eliminated. On the other hand, a few passages are so fundamentally different that the only explanation can be sought in differences in the original texts. But I wish to stress explicitly that none of these cases has any technical significance. In addition, the following should be considered: If—beyond differences in time, space, and religious beliefs—all translations describe the same structures, functions, and events, then that too makes it unnecessary to ask the opinion of yet another language expert.

Two aspects must be taken into account in the interpretation: One is Ezekiel's attitude as observer, the other his inner reaction to what he saw. The latter undergoes a drastic change, which is characterized by the transition from the shock effect of the first encounter to a cool and objective position. His attitude as observer is one of constant and admirable objectivity and accuracy, which could not be entirely suppressed even by the shock effect at the end of the first encounter. Consistent with this attitude he gives a full technical description of the spacecraft—in addition to the description of the events—only in his reports of the first encounter.

Regarding the *manner* in which Ezekiel describes what he has seen, we must bear in mind that, especially during the first encounter, he was exposed to an experience that lay far beyond anything he had ever seen before. He found himself in the situation of an intelligent but completely isolated man, so to speak. That was why he not only could not understand what he saw—he also lacked the very words to define what he saw. In later encounters his situation had changed insofar as at least the spaceship and the commander were no longer new to him. One factor, however, remains unchanged as far as Ezekiel is concerned: Neither he nor his contemporaries or forebears had any applicable or comparable technical knowledge or experience. Therefore, the only way was for him to describe what he saw to his contemporaries and to posterity by using similarities with objects or images familiar to himself and to the people of his time. Any one of us would do the same in a similar situation. In fact we did experience such a situation quite recently when we tried to describe what is now called UFO's by the simile "flying saucers."

Finally a few words about the general arrangement of the following passages. The subdivision of the Biblical text in Chapter and Verse was of course retained, as was also their order of sequence. I have, however, introduced general divisions that follow Ezekiel's encounters with the spaceships. These divisions in accordance with encounters improve both the clarity of the overall picture and the interrelation of details.

The first encounter

1:1. In the thirtieth year, in the fourth month, on the fifth day of the month, as I was among the exiles by the river Chebar, the heavens were opened, and I saw visions of God.

1:2. On the fifth day of the month (it was the fifth year of the exile of king Jehoiachim),

1:3. The word of the Lord came to Ezekiel the priest, the son of Buzi, in the land of the Chaldeans by the river Chebar; and the hand of the Lord was upon him there.

Verses 1 and 2: Already in his introductory verses Ezekiel demonstrates his inclination toward accurate definition by giving the exact date of the first encounter. It is the fifth day of the fourth month of the fifth year after the deportation of the Jews of Chaldea—which is the year 593 or 592 B.C. His additional mention of the thirtieth year is sometimes considered as a reference to the age of the prophet, but the commentators are not unanimous on this point. Ezekiel's attention is drawn to the spaceship by the firing of its rocket engine. As we have seen, the firing of the engine reduces the descent velocity of the spaceship to a rate low enough for the helicopters to take over the rest of the flight until the landing. The blast of the luminous plume of the engine must indeed have given Ezekiel the impression that "the heavens were opened."

Verse 3: As explained later, the words "the hand of the Lord was upon him there" always introduce—as a kind of leitmotif—the encounter with the spaceship and its commander.

1:4. As I looked, behold, a stormy wind came out of the north, and a great cloud, with brightness round about it, and fire flashing forth continually, and in the midst of the fire, as it were gleaming bronze.

1:5. And from the midst of it came the likeness of four living creatures. And this was their appearance: They had the form of men,

1:6. But each had four faces, and each of them had four wings.

1:7. Their legs were straight, and the soles of their feet were round; and they sparkled like burnished bronze.

Verse 4: Before the rocket engine can be ignited, the whole system of suction lines, pumps, etc., must be cooled down to the low temperature of liquid hydrogen in order to achieve the necessary working conditions.

This is done by forcing liquid hydrogen under pressure from the tank through the system. Hydrogen is eventually discharged into the atmosphere as a very cold gas. The water contained in the air (in the form of humidity) freezes into ice crystals and becomes visible in the form of a cloud—as it may sometimes be observed in high-flying jets. The duration of this chill-down process depends on the size of the engine, but lasts at least for many seconds so that a sizable cloud can be formed. The main body of the spacecraft that falls into this cloud, so to speak, forces it by its shape to flow radially outward, and thus the vehicle actually looks as though it were coming out of a cloud. As a result of the high descent velocity this cloud is visible over a considerable area when the engine is ignited.

Those who have seen the start of a Saturn rocket on television or film, or those who had the overwhelming experience of actually witnessing it, seeing it with their own eyes, can understand how aptly Ezekiel has described the optical effect of the plume. Nobody will ever forget the "fire flashing forth," the "brightness round about it," a shine "as it were gleaming bronze." Incidentally, it is only in *this* Verse 4 (besides Verse 1: "the heavens were opened") that Ezekiel describes the operation of the rocket engine—that is, the landing after a descent from an orbit around the earth. In all later encounters he saw the spacecraft only as a helicopter.

Verse 5: Ezekiel sees the four shapes in "the midst," that is, seemingly inside the fire, for two reasons. First one must realize that, contrary to the Saturn which flies *upward* away from the plume, for instance, the spaceship observed by Ezekiel falls *downward,* that is, into this cloud. Portions of slower but still hot outer zones of the plume encompass the vehicle, which makes it seem to be surrounded by flames. The second reason derives from the location of the spot where Ezekiel is standing relative to the trajectory of the spaceship, which contributes to the impression that the shapes are in "the midst of it." As shown by the following events, the spaceship lands at a short distance from him. Thus, as long as the rocket is firing, Ezekiel sees the spaceship coming almost directly toward him, which means that he sees it from below. This position enhances even more the impression of a firestorm surrounding the approaching vehicle.

In this and in the following verses Ezekiel describes what he saw; he does not describe the phases of the flight. At the moment of the (unmentioned) cutoff of the engine, the spacecraft is still some 3000 feet from where he stands. At this distance—and even somewhat farther—Ezekiel can already distinguish the "likenesses." The helicopter bodies, in combination with the rotating blades, first prompt him to choose the expression "living creatures," which is truly excellent in all its lack of precision. Ezekiel sees these living creatures in the midst of *fire,* which means that the engine is still in operation. Thus he confirms that the helicopters were deployed into their operating position before the engine was cut off. As the spaceship approaches, he is able to distinguish further details pertaining to the "living creatures," which prompt him to compare them to "the form of men." But this is only a passing impression. Now and until the end of the encounter he will refer to the helicopters with the fittingly vague expression "living creatures."

Verse 6: The spaceship is now at a low altitude or hovering above the ground. At any rate the observer is close enough to see the four blades of the rotors and to recognize various structural details which, to him, look like faces.

Verse 7: The description of the landing legs with their straight shock absorbers and their round footpads is altogether unmistakable (Figs. 1, 2, and 4).

1:8. Under their wings on their four sides they had human hands. And the four had their faces and their wings thus:

1:9. Their wings touched one another; they went every one straight forward, without turning as they went.

1:10. As for the likeness of their faces, each had the face of a man in front; the four had the face of a lion on the right side, the four had the face of a bull on the left side, and the four had the face of an eagle at the back.

Verse 8: The first sentence refers to the mechanical arms which are attached to and hang alongside the cylindrical bodies. The second sentence is continued in the next verse, in which it is mentioned that the creatures "went." The procedure described here belongs to Verse 15 and will be discussed in connection with that verse.

Verse 10: What prompted Ezekiel to see "faces"? As we know from the technical description of the spaceship, the gears and control mechanisms located immediately above the rotor plane are protected by a fairing. The latter has an irregular shape and is provided with protrusions and cutouts. Such a combination of structural features can assume a certain resemblance to faces or can best be described by such a comparison.

In support of this statement I would like to refer to facial and other features which all of us have seen in trees, rocks, and mountain skylines. I know a number of mountains in Europe and America whose names range broadly from "Sleeping Napoleon" to "Sleeping Indian Chief," depending on the image they suggest. Beyond that, however, much more concrete examples of the same kind may be found in the realm of most modern technology. Fig. 13a shows a Gemini capsule shortly after landing. I do not think that anyone can avoid the impression of looking at an abysmally solemn face. Even the view of that same capsule shown in Fig. 13b could hardly be described by somebody completely unfamiliar with technical structures otherwise than through its resemblance to a peculiar face or head. And who would not notice the monsterlike appearance of Lunochod 1 (Fig. 14), with its eyes, the open mouth, and the threateningly raised arms?

Even we who possess technical knowledge can thus see faces, heads, and bodies in such technical products. How much stronger must the impact of such visual associations have been on Ezekiel who had no technical knowledge at all. Even if he knew or sensed *what* he was looking at, he could still use only pictorial examples for conveying his impressions.

There may be yet another explanation which is less probable but still conceivable. Over the years, Ezekiel

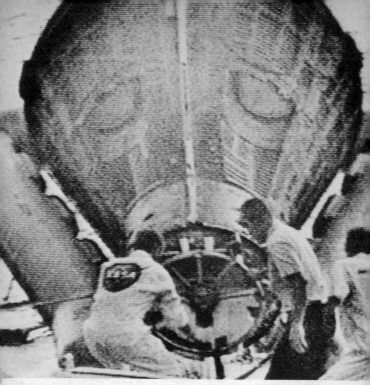

Figure 13a   Gemini capsule, front view

had repeated occasions to see the commander of the
spaceship and the members of that expedition, all of
whom looked like men to him. If we assume then that
the physical resemblance to humans also had its psychological parallel, it is entirely thinkable that these
beings at that time did what our pilots so often do today:
paint or otherwise depict faces, birds, and so on, on the
nose or sides of the fuselages of their aircraft just for
fun. After all, they were intelligent beings: Should they
necessarily have had less sense of humor than we have
today?

Whatever may have prompted Ezekiel to see faces or
describe as faces what he saw, his statements contain an

Figure 13b   Gemini capsule, aboard the recovery ship

Figure 14   Lunokhod 1

important point of information, namely, the confirmation of the same orientation of these "faces" on all helicopters: the face of a lion on the right side, the face of a steer on the left side, etc. If we maintain the assumption of facelike structural shapes, it necessarily follows that the four rotors were synchronized because their position at rest was the same.

1:11. And their faces and their wings were spread out above; each creature had two wings, each of which touched the wing of another, while two covered their bodies.

1:12. And each went straight forward; wherever the spirit would make them go, they went, without turning as they went.

1:13. In the midst of the living creatures there was something that looked like burning coals of fire, like torches moving to and fro among the living creatures; and the fire was bright, and out of the fire went forth lightning.

1:14. And the living creatures darted to and fro, like a flash of lightning . . .

Verse 11: The passage "their faces and their wings were spread out above" reads in References 1 and 2: "and their faces and wings upward were divided." The inclusion of the faces in this passage reflects an interesting observation. Before dealing with it in detail, it is useful to read the remainder of the verse which unmistakably describes the rotor blades folded upward and downward.

Reverting to the first part of the sentence, we observe that the words "spread out" (in the text used here) and "divided" (as in References 1 and 2) do not seem to have any close relationship to each other. However, if we rely for clarification more on the word "divided," we find a hint in the folded position of the two upper wings: Their arrangement suggests a slit, a long vertical gap. With that meaning in mind, we find that the expression "spread out" is related to "kept asunder" and "divided," and thus also includes an indication of a slit, a gap. There must indeed be some kind of a gap in the control mechanism or its fairing, both of which are located above the rotor plane. More specifically, there must be two slits or gaps, one for each of the two upper rotor blades and the shafts at their roots respectively. Room is needed for the wings to rotate from their horizontal working position to their almost vertical resting position. That seemingly unimportant detail was already mentioned in the technical description. The considerations just mentioned are significant not only for the correctness of the technical interpretation but even more so as an indication of the prophet's altogether exceptional talent for observation.

Verse 12: This verse reveals its full meaning—as does Verse 9—in connection with Verse 15 and will therefore be discussed together with the latter.

Verse 13: Ezekiel observes the space between the helicopters: He sees the glowing radiator of the reactor and the flickering of the control rockets. Considering the high temperature of the radiator, the comparison with "burning coals of fire" is correct and apposite. Control rockets function in short bursts and in seemingly irregular order. Source and direction of flashes change all the time. Such swift variations would produce in an unprepared observer the impression of "lightning" as it went "to and fro among the living creatures."

As seen from Ezekiel's position, two helicopters are located behind the main body of the spaceship. Because of their optical proximity to the glowing radiator of the reactor, the brief fiery blazes of the control rockets must give the impression of lightning which "went forth out of the fire."

Verse 14: The commander moves the spaceship in a hover flight in various directions as he looks for a suitable landing site. It is certain that the great bulk of the spaceship could not really move as fast as lightning. Up to a degree, an illusion could be responsible for this description—however, this would not be really satisfactory. A different solution will be discussed in Section 7.

1:15. Now as I looked at the living creatures, I saw a wheel upon the earth beside the living creatures, one for each of the four of them.

1:16. As for the appearance of the wheels and their construction: their appearance was like the gleaming of a Tarsis stone; and the four had the same likeness, their construction was as· though one wheel were within another.

1:17. When they went, they went in any of their four directions without turning as they went.

1:18. The four wheels had rims; and their rims were full of eyes round about.

1:19. And when the living creatures went, the wheels went beside them; and when the living creatures rose from the earth, the wheels rose.

1:20. Wherever the spirit would make them go, they went, for the spirit made them go; and the wheels rose along with them; for the spirit of the living creatures was in the wheels.

1:21. When those went, these went; and when those stood, these stood; and when those rose from the earth, the wheels rose along with them; for the spirit of the living creatures was in the wheels.

Verse 15: The spacecraft has landed. The landing legs have performed their task and the commander can now deploy the wheels that will be needed for subsequent operations. The fact that the wheels could indeed be deployed and retracted is demonstrated through the following consideration: Permanently fixed wheels would have been located somewhat below and to the side of the cylindrical helicopter bodies during the flight maneuvers performed so far. In that position, because of their shape and size, they would have been much more conspicuous and recognizable than the landing legs and mechanical arms; beyond any doubt Ezekiel would have described them together with these structures. Moreover, with the exception of some misplaced Verses, Ezekiel describes all the parts he saw in the order that corresponds to the phases of the landing process. While not mentioned as such, these phases can very well be directly followed through the text. Ezekiel begins with the fire and the clouds of the braking phase; then he describes the helicopters during the aerodynamic flight, and the radiator of the reactor and the control rockets as the spaceship is hovering; he then observes the functioning of the wheels and the rolling on the ground. Thus, the wheels appear in the text at the very place where they become necessary from a functional point of view. This sequence is an additional confirmation that the wheels were retractable, and further proof of the accuracy of the description.

Verses 16–21: As a first impression, the color of the wheels is described by a comparison with that of a mineral; in so describing it, Ezekiel draws a clear distinction between color and substance, because he explicitly says "like" the color of a Tarsis stone. Therefore it was quite clear to him that the wheels were not really made of Tarsis stone, but that its color was useful for their description.

This reference or comparison material is identified as follows by the various translators:

References	1:16
1, 2	turquoise
3, 7	chrysolith
4	topaz
5	Tarsis stone
6	beryl (with reference to topaz)

All these minerals have more or less a common hue —from greenish to bluish. With all the discrepancies in names one can recognize a light green-blue or blue-green as the color of the wheels. The surface was very smooth since it is described as glittering. This is most probably the appearance of a coat of paint or of some filmlike coating intended as a corrosion protection. Synthetic film coatings of this type are now used on a large scale for temporary corrosion protection. Some of them have an appearance exactly like the one described by Ezekiel when applied to machined steel or aluminum surfaces.

We know from the technical description why each "tire" is turned in itself while the wheel is turning as a whole. In the Appendix there is a description of a different wheel design, which includes additional drive disks that rotate to cause the separate turning of the tires. The "eyes" on the tires make the rotation even more conspicuous and underscore the independence of the movements from one another. The simultaneous rotation in several directions is confusing and a puzzle for a technically untrained observer. It creates the paradoxical illusion that there is more than one wheel in the wheel. Again, Ezekiel finds an unusually exact term by describing the appearance "as though one wheel were within another." The common English translation "wheel within a wheel" conveys an even clearer picture than the wording in the version used here.

Changes in rotation and direction occur in all four wheels simultaneously. They must give the impression that they are obeying orders. It is therefore only natural for Ezekiel to confuse, as it were, cause and effect; he considers the "living creatures" as those who move primarily and by whose side the wheels merely follow the motion. This is the mode of operation of the wheels he is familiar with. That the wheel itself can provide impetus for movement was unknown in his own time and for more than another two thousand years. Ezekiel's "spirit" is therefore much closer to the truth than he could ever have assumed.

The text devotes particularly long passages to the wheels. On the one hand this is due to obvious repetitions, but, on the other hand, also to the fact that the wheels, despite their confusing movements, were the only components of the overpowering phenomenon which Ezekiel knew, at least in their elementary form, and the normal functions of which he was familiar with. But precisely because he had had experience with ordinary wheels, he was all the more puzzled by their astonishing ability to change direction without any turning. One distinctly feels how he mistrusted his own observation: Maybe, since there is no movement of the wheel relative to the cylindrical helicopter body, the whole unit can be turned? He examines it and arrives at the negative conclusion of Verses 9 and 12: "they went every one straight forward, (And each went straight forward . . .) without turning as they went."

As for the purpose of the rolling (hence of the wheels), no specific motive can be determined at this time and therefore only assumptions are possible. So it is conceivable, for example, that the commander may have wished to improve the position of the spaceship on an uneven terrain: His vehicle has four pairs of legs—two legs to each helicopter. Therefore it is much more sensitive to the unevenness of the ground than if it had only three pairs. This sensitivity is avoidable, however, by a correct design and can therefore not be regarded as the reason for rolling. A plausible explanation is provided by the assumption of a *planned* mobility on the ground. Such mobility would, of course, not be needed in the sense of a vehicular motion; it could, however, be welcome or necessary for the transmission of signals: For communication between two ground stations by optical contacts (light, laser beams), and also whenever high-frequency radio equipment is used, a linear uninterrupted optical line of communication is indispensable. With the help of the wheels such "fine adjustment" becomes possible.

Verse 18 has different translations which read as follows in the texts I have used:

References	1:18
1, 2	Their rims and height were terrible; and their rims were full of eyes all around on all four wheels.
3	The four wheels had rims and they had spokes; and their rims were full of eyes round about.
4	No pertinent statement.
5	They also had rims. I looked and behold —their rims were full of eyes all around on the four of them.
6	As for their rings, they were high and they were dreadful; and they four had their rings full of eyes round about.
7	The four of them had rims, and I saw their rims were full of eyes all around.

This listing shows two groups, one of which speaks of the height and the dreadful aspect of the rims, while the other does not make such a statement. This difference is doubtless the result of the use of different original texts. The only translation mentioning spokes is Reference 3. However, all these discrepancies obviously do not affect the fundamental statements concerning the wheel.

1:22. Over the heads of the living creatures there was the likeness of a firmament, shining like rock crystal, spread out above their heads.

1:23. And under the firmament their wings were stretched out straight, one toward another; and each creature had two wings covering its body.

Verse 22: Here we find a description of the main body of the spacecraft. The geometrical shape and the position of the helicopters relative to the main body can hardly be better characterized: "Over the heads of the living

creatures . . . likeness of a firmament . . . spread
out above their heads." How superbly the depiction of
the general impression is conveyed and, specifically, how
well the form of the main body is reflected in the passage
"spread out above," is best illustrated by a comparison
of these texts with Figs. 1, 2, and 4.

Although color descriptions are somewhat divergent
in the various translations since mention is made of
"crystal" (References 1, 2, 3, 7), "rock crystal" (Reference 5), and also of "terrible ice" (Reference 6), all
descriptions convey the optical picture of a very smooth,
very bright, shining surface characteristic of certain al-
loys.

Verse 23: The text is incomplete. The first part of the
sentence offers an additional description of the position
of the helicopters with reference to the main body. The
placement of the rotors "under" the arch so aptly described as "firmament" conveys a very clear picture. The
term "firmament" is even more understandable if we
realize that Ezekiel did not see the spaceship in its technical projection (as in Fig. 4) but rather, from where he
stood, with a perspective view (as in Fig. 1). If, in addition, we compare his size with that of the mighty arch of
the central body, it becomes quite understandable how
the spaceship could suggest to him the image of "firmament." The second part of the sentence is doubtless a
fragment of which only the final portion has been preserved. It repeats the earlier description of the rotor
blades in resting position.

1:24. And when they went, I heard the sound of their
wings like the sound of many waters, like the thunder of the Almighty, a sound of tumult like the
sound of a host; when they stood still, they let
down their wings.

1:25. And there came a sound from above the firmament over their heads; when they stood still, they
let down their wings.

Verse 24 and also Verse 25 do not really belong here,
because they describe the still running rotors and attending phenomena, while Verse 23 already gave a descrip-

tion of the position at rest. This information is part of the description of the hover flight and the subsequent landing, and should therefore be inserted between Verses 14 and 15.

From a technical point of view the reference to "the sound of many waters" is a good comparison with the somewhat hissing sound of the rotating rotor blades. The "thunder of the Almighty" and the "sound of a host" become understandable if we realize that, after all, the power required by the helicopters was 70,000 horsepower or more, which is an order of magnitude productive, at any rate, of some considerable noise. Ezekiel makes the very important observation that the really loud noise—the sound of a host—begins when the rotor blades begin to move; because at that moment power is increased rapidly from idling up to its full amount, which is of course accompanied by a commensurate increase in noise. The folding of the rotor blades is only noted with regard to the pair folding downward; Ezekiel's statement is nonetheless significant when he says: "when they stood still, they let down their wings." His observation is correct: this procedure occurs only when the spaceship is on the ground and the rotors have come to a standstill.

Verse 25 is yet another example of the almost incredible power of observation with which the prophet was endowed. He notices a "sound from above the firmament." As seen from his position, the larger portion of the interior of the spaceship was indeed *above* the arched surface of the main body—what he hears, therefore, is the sound of the idling central power plant of the helicopters, which is located in that area. This amazing statement is expressed even better in Reference 6, but finds its clearest expression in References 1 and 2; there we read: "and when they stood and let down their wings, there was thunder in the firmament above them." This version suggests the incredible possibility that at this point Ezekiel had already recognized a relationship, or at least had sensed it by intuition. Whether this surmise is correct remains of course a question to which no answer can be given.

1:26. And above the firmament over their heads there was the likeness of a throne, in appearance like sapphire; and seated above the likeness of a throne was a likeness as the appearance of a man upon it above.

Verse 26: Looking up beyond the rim of the "firmament," Ezekiel sees the command capsule. The first object he notices is the commander's seat and he begins its description by mentioning its color. As he did earlier, he refers to a mineral for this purpose; and again he differentiates between appearance and substance by using the word "like." The comparison to a throne which follows is interesting and revealing. On the one hand it indicates that Ezekiel himself had probably seen a throne; this is quite plausible because he belonged to a Jewish group of high social standing. If, however, we consider the most characteristic features of a throne—the high back, its arm rests, and possibly its upholstery—we will have no difficulty identifying them with the passenger seats and especially the pilot seats of present-day airliners. The word "throne" thus clearly defines the seat of the commander.

In connection with the seats of our present-day aircraft it should not be overlooked that even their color is often consistent with Ezekiel's description. We cannot explore here whether this is merely coincidental or whether psychological factors are also relevant in the choice of colors. The latter case would notably broaden the scope of those visitors' resemblance to humans, an aspect that is discussed later in this book.

The second part of the Verse takes us to the very peak of Ezekiel's capabilities: he sees the shape of the commander who is sitting on the "throne," and acknowledges in him "a likeness as the appearance of a man."

To understand the true extent of the intellectual effort that was necessary to make such a statement, we must again turn our attention to the situation in which Ezekiel found himself. Without any warning an event burst upon him, he was suddenly confronted by an object and by occurrences for which he had nothing in the way of comparison, reference, or logical explanation within the whole range of what he had ever known or felt. As he is a believer, and a priest, he has every reason—at least during this phase of the first encounter—to believe that the commander is God himself. The mass of impressions which he suddenly receives shakes him to his innermost depths. But in the midst of this tumult of his senses— he is in a near shock condition—his spirit is yet not overcome by his emotions. He retains the incredible ability to register in his brain with full objectivity what his eyes actually see; and he is capable of describing later in the same objective manner what he saw. Only an intellect of superior caliber is capable of such an achievement!

Another weighty circumstance must be mentioned here: Rabbi Dr. Fisch explicitly points out in his commentary (Reference 6, p. 41) that Ezekiel uses in his description of the commander's appearance the word "Adam." With that, Ezekiel himself eliminates any possibility of a different interpretation.

1:27. I saw as it were gleaming bronze, as the appearance of fire round about enclosing him. Upward from what had the appearance of his loins, and downward from what had the appearance of his loins, I saw as it were the appearance of fire, and there was brightness round about him.

1:28. Like the appearance of the bow that is in the cloud on the day of rain, so was the appearance of the brightness round about. Such was the appearance of the likeness of the glory of the Lord. And when I saw it, I fell upon my face, and I heard the voice of one that spoke.

Verse 27: In this Verse (and in the beginning of Verse 28) Ezekiel—because of his natural lack of pertinent knowledge—aptly differentiates two objects through the quality of their light effects. One is characterized by "fire" and "gleaming bronze," the other by "brightness" and "bow" (rainbow). The difference between these two optical effects—the active, penetrating effect of fire, the static transparency of the rainbow—indicates two origins, two different objects as sources of these effects. This realization helps in the unraveling of these passages which would otherwise appear rather confusing.

Both the text (with its reference to "loins") and the technical necessity lead us to recognize in the words "fire" and "gleaming bronze" the commander's suit, the surface of which has a gilded appearance. The aptness of the description chosen by Ezekiel is reminiscent of the lively light effects and flamelike reflections of the insulation of an Apollo lunar module. The goldlike appearance of this insulation is produced by a special, very thin synthetic foil which is covered on its inward side by an equally thin aluminum coating. This outer sheet is the topmost of many similar layers which jointly serve as protection against undesirably high temperatures. Thus we can witness today the use of such materials and protective layers. There is no valid reason against the assumption that the suit worn by the commander was in its outer layer very much like the one shown here.

Very different from this is the optical effect of the capsule, which is made of a glasslike material. Its light and color effect is confusing: Sunlight hits it directly, but there is also the glare from the rays reflected from the curved upper side of the spaceship. A part of its surface mirrors the blue of the sky while Ezekiel can see the sky through other parts of the capsule. To this are added the fiery reflections of the commander's suit and the sapphire hue of his seat. Additional color effects may be caused by interference phenomema of the doubtlessly laminated material of the capsule. When Ezekiel describes this variety of light and hues as "brightness round about him," he gives a very good image of what he saw; and also the comparison with the rainbow becomes understandable.

Finally, we should not overlook the fact that all this brightness was "round about him" and therefore did not proceed from him. Again we have a case where observation coincides exactly with actual fact: The capsule *surrounds* the commander, it is "round about" him. As for the rest, there is nothing else about the capsule that is unusual and would prompt Ezekiel to make further statements; except, perhaps, its curved upper part which suggests a comparison with a rainbow.

With these last remarks Ezekiel has reached the end of his observations and descriptions of the visible phenomena. He contemplates again, as it were, the total picture when he says by way of summary: "Such was the appearance of the likeness of the glory of the Lord."

Overwhelmed, he falls with his face to the ground. Yet his undeceivable spirit is still awake: Although he had every reason to qualify what he has seen as the "glory of the Lord" and although such an expression would be entirely understandable at this point, he still expresses two reservations at this moment. He cannot reconcile the massive, real apparition of the spacecraft with a manifestation of the Lord, which he would not expect to be so utterly material. He does not know what he is really seeing, yet whatever it may be, it is colossal, mighty, and overpowering—it seems to be *comparable* to the glory of the Lord. And this is precisely what he says: "Such was the appearance of the *likeness* of the glory of the Lord." There is no doubt about it—he does not identify, he compares. The second reservation concerns the voice he hears. Again one could expect and understand him to believe that he was hearing the voice of the Lord. But Ezekiel again stays aloof and in very sober terms states what he hears: ". . . the voice of *one* that spoke"; he avoids any tendency to glorify, to be sensational, and quite simply says: ". . . one that . . ."

> **2:9.** And when I looked, behold, a hand was stretched out to me, and lo, a written scroll was in it;
> **2:10.** and he spread it before me; . . .

In Chapter 2 only Verse 9 and the first words of Verse 10 are of consequence here. Ezekiel sees the hand of a mechanical arm before him. Since a scroll cannot be opened and spread out by one hand, we find at the beginning of Verse 10 a reference to another mechanical arm. This reference is fully consistent with Verse 8 of Chapter 1: "Under their wings on their four sides they had human hands."

3:12. Then the spirit lifted me up, and as the glory of the Lord arose from its place, I heard behind me the sound of a great earthquake;

3:13. It was the sound of the wings of the living creatures as they touched one another, and the sound of the wheels beside them that sounded like a great earthquake.

Verse 12: For the first time Ezekiel is flying in a spaceship! He was lifted into the command capsule in a not clearly defined way and finds himself now at the uppermost point of the spaceship. Since the vehicle is moving vertically upward, Ezekiel hears the noise of the central power plant literally behind him. Through his seat he is now in close bodily contact with the vehicle; he feels therefore its vibrations which, lacking any applicable experience, he compares with "a great earthquake." While he is still aware of all this, the spaceship —"the glory of the Lord"—lifts up from the ground.

Verse 13: Ezekiel cannot see the rotors from where he sits, but he recognizes their noise again because he describes it as "the sound of the wings of the living creatures." With all the noise going on, he certainly cannot perceive "the sound of the wheels." Besides, helicopters usually start without any rolling. However, in such a large structure with a huge surface there are reverberations of many sounds that could have induced Ezekiel to make this comparison.

3:14. The spirit lifted me up and took me away, and I went in bitterness in the heat of my spirit, the hand of the Lord being strong upon me;

3:15. And I came to the exiles at Tel-Abib, who dwelt by the river Chebar. And I sat there overwhelmed among them seven days.

Verse 14: Ezekiel is now aware that he is flying. He is overcome by the full impact of the shock produced by this experience. The "hand of the Lord" which he feels as "strong upon me" could simply have been the pressure of the shoulder straps holding him to his seat. On the other hand, this is again the expression that we have already noted in Chapter 1, Verse 3, and which invariably is used whenever a meeting with the commander is forthcoming. The question of whether that implies some hypnotic or other influence on Ezekiel's thoughts or emotions falls outside the scope of this investigation.

Verse 15: Ezekiel's condition upon his arrival in Tel-Abib is depicted by varying expressions in the different translations; they range from "most sad" to "distraught" and in all cases point to a severe mental shock. It took him seven days to recover from it.

The second encounter

3:22. And the hand of the Lord was there upon me; and he said to me: "Arise, go forth into the plain, and there I will speak to you."

3:23. So I arose and went forth into the plain; and lo, the glory of the Lord stood there, like the glory which I had seen by the river Chebar; and I fell on my face.

3:24. But the spirit entered into me, and set me upon my feet; and he spoke with me and said to me . . .

Verse 22: The time of this encounter cannot be determined exactly. From the date of the third encounter it follows that a period somewhat longer than a year elapsed between it and the first encounter. The timing of the second encounter is thereby established at least to a certain degree. The introduction to the events occurs again in the manner already familiar to us by the mention of the "hand of the Lord."

Verse 23: Ezekiel follows the order to go to the plain; there he sees a phenomenon which he describes as "the glory which I had seen by the river Chebar." As he did then, now too he falls on his face. This indicates that he saw the landed spaceship again and also recognized it. He does not devote a single word to its description, however.

Verse 24: As in the first encounter, he feels restored and strengthened. The nontechnical contents of this encounter end abruptly with Chapter 7 without any indica-

tion of how it was terminated. It is interesting to note
that here again Ezekiel refers to the commander without
any reverence—just: ". . . he spoke with me . . ."

The third encounter

8:1. In the sixth year, in the sixth month, on the fifth
day of the month, as I sat in my house, with the
elders of Judah sitting before me, the hand of the
Lord God fell there upon me.

8:2. Then I beheld, and lo, a form of what had the
appearance of a man; below what appeared to be
his loins it was like fire, and above his loins it was
like the appearance of brightness, like gleaming
bronze.

8:3. He put forth the form of a hand, and took me by
a lock of my head; and the spirit lifted me up between earth and heaven, and brought me in visions
of God to Jerusalem, to the entrance of the gateway of the inner court that faces north, where was
the seat of the image of jealousy, which provokes
to jealousy.

8:4. And behold, the glory of the God of Israel was
there, like the vision that I saw in the plain.

Verse 1: A little more than a year has gone by since
Ezekiel's first encounter with the spacecraft and its commander; an undetermined period of probably several
months separates him from the second encounter. The
announcement of the event is again expressed by the
characteristic phrase: ". . . the hand of the Lord God
fell there upon me."

Verses 2 and 3: These Verses are evidently a remainder of an originally longer passage. They do contain a description of the commander in terms very similar
to Chapter 1, Verse 27, and also mention the mechanical
arm as "the form of a hand." However, because of
passages missing in the texts before and after Verse 2 as
well as in Verse 3, the statement is merely a fragment.
This mutilated text is not understandable without knowledge of earlier descriptions and technical reconstruc-

tions, and can even be misleading. Ezekiel flies "between earth and heaven" to Jerusalem and is not moved to a state of excitement by either the encounter or the flight. In that regard the contrast with the first encounter is almost unbelievable and it indicates that Ezekiel's exceptional intellect has correctly judged and digested the situation. He is put on the ground in the vicinity of the northern gate of the temple.

Verse 4: From the preceding mutilated Verses the conclusion could be drawn that Ezekiel was flying with the capsule alone and not with the whole spacecraft. However, once back on the ground, he confirms the presence of the *whole* vehicle: ". . . like the vision that I saw in the plain." It is noteworthy that he confirms this identity only with respect to the spaceship but not to the commander.

9:1. Then he cried in my ears with a loud voice, saying: "Draw near you executioners of the city, each with his destroying weapon in his hand."

Verse 1: After the introduction just discussed the action now assumes very dramatic forms. The commander who remains in the capsule together with Ezekiel apparently uses a loudspeaker which strikes the ears of the prophet "with a loud voice." The statement: "Draw near you executioners of the city" has had different translations:

References	9:1
1, 2	Let the hardship come
3	Draw near you executioners
4	[No relevant commentary]
5	The tribulations are drawing near
6	Cause ye them that have charge over the city
7	Come, you scourges of the city

As this survey shows, there may be two interpretations of the fundamental meaning of the passage: the meaning of a statement of fact (. . . are drawing near) and that of a command (come . . .). Moreover, there is a difference in the characterization of those addressed. It is not clear whether executioners are meant or people who have charge over the city. The unraveling of this knot begins with Reference 6. We learn there, on page 41, that the Hebrew text lends itself to all these interpretations. Moreover, we realize from the progress of the action that this passage is indeed a command. Finally, with respect to the administrative status of the persons called upon, the version in Reference 6—where they are described as having charge over the city—would appear to be the most fitting. The scope and the meaning of that "charge" remain of course undefined, yet the assumption is permitted that the city was placed under the persons called upon for some unknown task. Status and task of these men are not relevant to our technical study. However, we shall revert to these points in section 8 in another context.

The second part of the command demands that everyone bring with him "his destroying weapon." It is of interest to explore this passage also in more depth. The following table lists the various expressions employed in the texts I have been using:

References	9:1	9:2
1	murder weapon	harmful weapon
2	murdering weapon	harmful weapon
3	destroying weapon	weapon for slaughter
4	. . .	. . .
5	tool of annihilation	tool of destruction
6	destroying weapon	weapon of destruction
7	[Sentence missing]	destroying weapon

The characteristic feature of this comparison is the evident ambiguity of the expression used in the original. This impression is further strengthened by the fact that the same implement receives different designations in two consecutive verses.

Now Ezekiel certainly well knew the weapons used in

his time. Even if the appropriate term could be misunderstood by him in the commander's order, he should
have recognized the weapons they carried when the persons summoned made their appearance—if those had
indeed been weapons in use at his time and in his environment! The use of a vague expression makes it clear,
however, that the objects he saw were unknown to him.
This becomes understandable in view of the ensuing
events.

> **9:2.** And lo, six men came from the direction of the
> upper gate, which faces north, every man with his
> weapon for slaughter in his hand, and in their
> midst was a man clothed in linen, with a writing
> case at his side. And they went in and stood beside
> the bronze altar.

Verse 2: The immediate arrival of the men is possible
only if they had been waiting for the summons on the
other side of the gate. This points to a prior arrangement
between the commander and the ground crew. We therefore can assume that radio communication existed between them. Such possibilities are a matter of course
even to us and have been so for many years. Their presence in this context is therefore in no way peculiar.

The fact that is peculiar and exciting is that Ezekiel—
despite his extraordinary talent for observation—finds
nothing unusual about these men except the "destroying
weapon." Not even the man in their midst impresses him
with anything other than that he was "clothed in linen."
If we add to this the fact that the commander too is always described simply as "man," it follows that all those
related to the spaceship looked like humans. This very
important observation will be treated in depth in section 8.

The man in clothes of linen deserves closer scrutiny
because of the functions he performs later. If we take
the description literally, such clothes mean a high rank
(Reference 6, p. 47). This is confirmed insofar as he
walks in the middle of the approaching group (Reference 5). And indeed, as events develop, this man assumes a special position; the activity incident upon it

makes it clear, however, that his clothes are in fact a suit protective at least against heat. Accordingly, its outer layer could have been made of asbestos, which would explain its linenlike appearance.

In contrast to the other men he does not carry an undefined "tool," but he has a "writing case at his side." Instead of "writing case" some translations contain the word "inkhorn," but the basic meanings are identical. I do not know whether high officials really used to carry a writing implement. The situation suggests that the man wearing the protective suit was carrying a device of *his* time, that is of a time of advanced space travel. It is therefore logical to suspect rather that the so-called writing implement was really a communication device or an instrument for radiation detection. A determination of such a likelihood lies outside my professional competence, but I hope that this question will be clarified by a cooperative research conducted by experts in cultural history and engineers specializing in telecommunications and radiation detection.

This whole somewhat mysterious group now proceeds to the "bronze" altar and takes position beside it.

9:3. Now the glory of the God of Israel had gone up from the Cherubim on which it rested, to the threshold of the house; and he called to the man clothed in linen, who had the writing case at his side.

9:4. And the Lord said to him: "Go through the city, Jerusalem, and put a mark upon the foreheads of the men who sigh and groan over all the abominations that are committed in it."

9:5. And to the others he said in my hearing: "Pass through the city after him, and smite; your eye shall not spare, and you shall show no pity; slay old men outright, your men and maidens, little children and women, but touch no one upon whom is the mark. And begin at my sanctuary."

9:11. And lo, the man clothed in linen, with the writing case at his side, brought back word, saying: "I have done as thou didst command me."

Verse 3: The beginning of this verse seems to convey the same content as the corresponding part of Verse 4 of Chapter 10: "And the glory of the Lord went up from the cherubim." A superficial assessment would show this passage as an unnecessary and misplaced repetition of Chapter 9, Verse 3. But in Chapter 9, Verse 3, Ezekiel speaks of the "glory of the God of Israel," while Chapter 10, Verse 4, refers to the "glory of the Lord." If we bear in mind Ezekiel's enormous gift of observation, such differentiation is not meaningless. It points to a difference between the two flying objects. It appears certain that Chapter 9, Verse 3, refers to the flight of the commander—and we shall find direct evidence of this as we discuss Chapter 10—while Chapter 10, Verse 4, concerns the flight of the empty capsule. As shown in section 4 of this book, both flights are possible today.

Thus the commander has flown to the temple, and he first summons to him the man "clothed in linen" who carried the "writing case."

Verse 4: Of all the passages of Ezekiel's book that have technical relevance this is the only one where the commander is directly identified with God ("the Lord"). This exceptional case is discussed in section 7 of this book. For the time being the only significant fact is that the commander gives an order to the man "clothed in linen." We shall revert to the content of that order in connection with Chapter 10, Verse 7.

Verse 5: The other men also receive assignments. A longer passage follows in the text which does not pertain to our investigation.

Verse 11: This verse comes back to the main events —the events concerning the commander and his helpers. This occurs in a very striking and exciting manner. The man in the protective suit comes back and reports: "I have done as thou didst command me." With these few words a situation is outlined with which we are very familiar: a report by a subordinate to a superior. It is short and matter-of-fact and recalls military brevity and discipline. Coming across such a situation under circumstances so remote from us in every sense confers upon this moment a staggering and truly electrifying quality.

10:1. Then I looked, and behold, on the firmament that was over the heads of the cherubim there appeared above them something like a sapphire, in form resembling a throne.

10:2. And he said to the man clothed in linen: "Go in among the wheels underneath the cherubim; fill your hands with burning coals from between the cherubim, and scatter them over the city." And he went in before my eyes.

10:3. Now the cherubim were standing on the right side of the house, when the man went in; and a cloud filled the inner court.

10:4. And the glory of the Lord went up from the cherubim to the threshold of the house; and the house was filled with the cloud, and the court was full of the brightness of the glory of the Lord.

10:6. And when he commanded the man clothed in linen: "Take fire from between the wheels, from between the cherubim," he went in and stood beside a wheel.

10:7. And a cherub stretched forth his hand from between the cherubim to the fire that was between the cherubim, and took some of it, and put it into the hands of the man clothed in linen, who took it and went out.

10:18. Then the glory of the Lord went forth from the threshold of the house, and stood over the cherubim.

Verse 1: Ezekiel looks over to the spaceship and makes an important observation. He briefly describes the position of the command capsule on top of the vehicle; but this description ends with the throne! No man is sitting on the throne. But none can be there, since the commander has flown to the temple as shown in the discussion of Chapter 9, Verse 3; has given his orders there and has also received there the report of the man in the protective suit. One has the impression that, after Ezekiel saw the commander flying to the temple, he now wants to make sure that this was indeed "his" commander. This is why he looks at the spaceship and finds his assumption confirmed: the "throne"—which is the commander's seat—is indeed empty! As before, we can only express the highest admiration for the precision of his observation and also the desire to check an observation that may be open to doubt.

At the place where it occurs in the text this Verse was inserted out of context and in fact disrupts the description of the progress of the action. It seems that it would best belong to Chapter 9, Verse 3.

Chapter 10 generally presents some difficulties in its structure. Although the action developed in Chapter 9 is continued here, as may be ascertained by careful reading, it is repeatedly interrupted by unrelated descriptions of the spacecraft. One has the impression of insertions or a rewriting done by persons not familiar with these events and we shall come back to this question later. At any rate, it is therefore better to select and discuss first the essential part of this chapter, that is, the action, and later to examine as a group the inserts that were not treated at the first reading. This essential part of the contents is to be found in Verses 2, 3, 4, 6, 7, 18, and 19, which will now be discussed.

Verse 2: The commander orders the man in the protective suit to go to the spaceship, to take some red-hot material from the main body ("from between the cherubim") and to scatter it "over the city." Now it becomes understandable why that man needed a protective suit: He had to come close to the large glowing surface of the radiator of the reactor which, naturally, was radiating intense heat. For the same reason the man also cannot move close to the main body and he is specifically instructed to remain "underneath the cherubim." Since, at that moment, the rotors are standing still, the word "underneath" does not mean that he would stand somewhere within the range of the rotor diameter, but rather refers—in defining the place where he is ordered to stand—to the body of the helicopters. A literal interpretation of the word "underneath" would only be possible if the lower edge of the helicopter body was high enough above the ground. In view of the large diameter of the wheels such height is entirely possible. At any rate, the order says that the place he was to stand in must be in the immediate vicinity of the helicopter. In Verse 6, we read later that the man stood "beside a wheel," which confirms the considerations above. The man was supposed to take something red-hot in his hands and to scatter it "over the city." The unclear last part of this command will be explained later. Besides, this Verse appears too early in the text. To be consistent with the course of events, it would belong to Verse 6.

Verse 3: Here we are given a description of the position of the spacecraft at the time the man approaches it. This description is given from where Ezekiel is standing. To derive from it a specific indication of the location of the vehicle relative to the temple, we must first try to identify Ezekiel's position. In Chapter 8, Verse 3, he says that he was standing in the courtyard near the north gate. From Chapter 9, Verse 2, one might conclude that he had moved somewhat away from it because he sees the men coming "from the direction of the upper gate." If now, in Chapter 10, Verse 3, he sees the spaceship "on the right side of the house"—which means to the right of the temple—then its position may be deduced with sufficient certainty to lie somewhat to the north of the temple.

The "cloud" is mentioned in a quite casual way, as though it had already been introduced and described at an earlier stage. It appears probable that this passage was inserted here too early, since its contents are repeated in Verse 4.

Verse 4: As was already mentioned in the discussion of Chapter 9, Verse 3, the capsule—operated by remote control by the commander—flies from the spaceship to the threshold of the temple. It is important to note that the commander is there too (see Chapter 9, Verse 3). In this context a "cloud" would be altogether conceivable; however, it would be a cloud of dust raised by the jets of the engines of the capsule. The addition "and the court was full of the brightness of the glory of the Lord" may describe the light effects produced by the glasslike and highly reflective surface of the capsule. The use of engines with hot gases—whose light effect could perhaps be suspected here—is ruled out because the capsule was brought to land next to the commander. Hot exhaust gases from rocket engines probably would have severely injured the commander.

Verse 6: According to the context, this would be the right moment for giving the final command. This is why —as we have already mentioned—Verse 2 could really belong *here*. At any rate, with the posting of the man next to the helicopter, all preparatory moves have been completed. Everyone and everything is now in position: The commander and his capsule are at the front side of the temple (which is its east side), the spaceship is on the north side, Ezekiel presumably is not very far from the north gate; the man in the protective suit takes his position "beside a wheel."

Verse 7: Now the mechanical arm—and of course there may be more than one arm involved—reaches its hand toward the main body of the spaceship, picks up something, and moves it across to the man standing by the wheel, who takes it with both hands and carries it away.

As for the burning question about what really took place here, some attempts at an answer can be made. Seen from a technical angle, one thing is certain— namely that some hot element was removed. Whether it was "hot" only in a thermal sense or also included nu- clear radiation is not clear.

More light can be shed on this matter by going back to the first two orders issued by the commander. If we study the essence of these orders given to the man in the protective suit and to the accompanying crew, we find that they involve the task of seeking and marking in the first instance, and that of removing undesirable things, obstacles, in the second. These fundamental ideas may be applied both in a religious and a technical sense. Doing this—in contrast to the Bible—in the technical sense, the following picture will emerge: We have just seen that a structural part or an element of the reactor had to be removed, either because of an emergency or

according to plan. In both cases, that is, whether it was
an emergency or a planned operation, the part to be
removed was "hot." It was therefore imperative to find
in advance a place where the part could be disposed of
safely and fast. Both activities, the search and marking
of that place as well as its preparation, such as, for example, the removal of earth, rocks, or bushes, are reflected in the basic meaning of the commands. Even the
continued absence of the six men could be explained by
their being engaged in the preparation and safeguarding
of this site. Finally, it should be pointed out that there
is an absence of any greetings between the commander
and the ground crew, and that the commands follow
each other in a brisk sequence. Both these circumstances
suggest a certain haste and urgency.

Verse 18 and 19: After the departure of the man
wearing the protective suit, the capsule returns without
any waste of time: It flies back to the main body. The
text that follows later indicates that the commander is
inside the capsule. Immediately upon his arrival, he
starts the helicopter because, as Ezekiel observes, they
"lifted up their wings." The helicopter, however, makes
only a short leap to the east gate.

The rapid sequence of events draws attention to their
peculiar interrelation. First the commander removes
Ezekiel—his passenger on that flight—from the spaceship; then he goes himself to the entrance to the temple,
which means that it is important to him to be at a certain distance from his spaceship. While the man in the
protective suit—having fulfilled his first task—proceeds
toward the spacecraft, even the capsule is removed from
it and flown to the commander who, it appears, soon
boards it; at any rate he flies in it back to the ship as
soon as the man in the protective suit has departed. One
cannot fail to notice that, at an obviously critical moment, nobody is in the immediate vicinity of the spaceship except the one indispensable assistant. We know,
moreover, that the commander was by the east side of
the temple while his spaceship stood to its north. One
cannot entirely escape the impression that in the course
of these preparations the commander very prudently

had put part of the temple between himself and the critical procedure which was being carried out on the spaceship. This impression is strengthened even more by the presence of the capsule by his side which—if needed—could provide him with a swift means of escape.

The analysis of those Verses in Chapter 10 which describe the action has now been completed. Other Verses include references to helicopters or confirm the identity of the vehicle; the description of the wheels again takes much space. With a single exception, descriptions are identical with those of the first encounter, so that repetition is not necessary. The start, however, is described more clearly than ever before:

10:16. . . . when the cherubim lifted up their wings to mount up from the earth, the wheels did not turn from beside them.

This describes how the rotor blades—with the specific objective "to mount up from the earth"—were brought into their horizontal working position for the start. With his admirable keenness of observation, Ezekiel describes this action and its motivation in a mere secondary clause pertaining to a description of the wheel.

The above mentioned single exception in the description relates to Verse 12, which reads as follows in the translations I used:

References	10:12
1	And their whole body, backs, hands and wings and the wheels were full of eyes round about; all four of them had wheels.
2	[End of 10:11] . . . they followed and they turned not . . . with their whole body, backs, hands and wings. And the wheels were full of eyes round about on all four wheels.
3	And their rims and their spokes, and the wheels were full of eyes round about— the wheels that the four of them had.
4	[No commentary]

5   But their whole body, their back, their
         hands, their wings and the wheels were
         full of eyes round about.

6   And their whole body, and their backs,
         and their hands, and their wings, and the
         wheels were full of eyes round about,
         even the wheels that they four had.

7   The rims of the four wheels were full of
         eyes all around.

It was explained in the technical description that "eyes" meant the wheel profile patterns that cause resistance to skidding. The text of Reference 7 corresponds to this view. All the others depart from it. Reference 6 comes to the following conclusion in its commentary on page 53: ". . . they do not refer to the cherubim, but to the various parts of the wheels; that is to say, the whole of the wheels was full of eyes." The meaning of this commentary is consistent with the translations given in References 2 and 3. The difficulty here seems to lie much more in the original text than in the translation.

With the exception of the translation in Reference 7, the text of Chapter 10, Verse 12, is therefore not in agreement with Chapter 1, Verse 18, because there we read without any ambiguity that ". . . their rims were full of eyes round about . . ." I derive some satisfaction from pointing out that we have the *only* case where two descriptions do not coincide. Everywhere else, whenever repetitions occur or subjects are described that have technical connotations, there is absolute consistency. This fact shows convincingly how well founded and consistent Ezekiel's report is.

But even in this single exception there is no contradiction but merely a lack of agreement. Two criteria help in the clarification of this case, one of literary and the other of a technical nature. From a literary viewpoint there is a juxtaposition between the quite clear structure of the first Chapter and the confused grouping of material in Chapter 10. The uncertainty reflected in the order of the Verses of Chapter 10 makes it appear less reliable than Chapter 1. Moreover, there is at least one translation in Chapter 10 that is practically identical with the Verse in Chapter 1. Viewed therefore from a literary angle, it is Verse 18 of Chapter 1, which reads ". . . their rims were full of eyes round about . . ." that has the greater weight. From a technical viewpoint this interpretation is undoubtedly the right one. Other interpretations disqualify themselves because none of the earlier descriptions of main body, capsule, and helicopters contain any reference whatsoever to "eyes." On the contrary. The main body is represented as being crystallike, the capsule as bright and reflective; both descriptions rule out any disruption of surfaces by structural patterns.

Therefore, the statement in Verse 12: "And their whole body, and their backs, and their hands, and their wings, and the wheels were full of eyes round about . . ." can be regarded with certainty as incorrect.

> **10:13.** As for the wheels, they were called in my hearing the "galgal" (wheel work).

Parts of the wheels appear to revolve faster than would seem consistent with the speed of their movement. In view of the wheel design (Fig. 10 and Appendix), the expression "wheel work" is a very fitting description of the separate rotation of the segments. Noteworthy is the hint of a conversation (". . . were called in my hearing . . ."). It may well be that this Verse should more appropriately have followed Verse 6 of Chapter 10 which includes the second order by the commander: "Take fire from between the wheels . . ." This fragmentary allusion to a conversation may of course also pertain to a lost portion of the document.

The account of the faces differs somewhat from that given in Chapter 1 where we read:

> **1:10.** As for the likeness of their faces, each had the face of a man in front; the four had the face of a lion on the right side, the four had the face of a bull on the left side, and the four had the face of an eagle at the back.

The translations compare as follows:

References   *1:10*

1	cherub	man	lion	eagle
2	cherub	man	lion	eagle
3	cherub	man	lion	eagle
4	a cherub	man	lion	eagle
	= ox			
5	bull	man	lion	eagle
6	cherub	man	lion	eagle
7	ox	man	lion	eagle

The order of the faces is the same in the texts of the two Chapters; there are, however, uncertainties with regard to the character of the first face which is variously given as that of a cherub, an ox, or a bull. From a technical viewpoint this uncertainty is relevant only insofar it indicates that the shape of the fairing in that area was complex and difficult to describe.

With regard to the faces Ezekiel says explicitly:

10:22. And as for the likeness of their faces, they were the very faces whose appearance I had seen by the river Chebar. They went everyone straight forward.

He also confirms the identity of the spaceship observed with the one of the first encounter:

10:20. This was the living creature that I saw underneath the God of Israel by the river Chebar; and I knew that they were cherubim.

The jump from the singular to the plural is quite conspicuous. However, References 3 and 7 use the plural in both cases. Nevertheless the version reproduced above prevails. It lends itself to an easy explanation if we relate the beginning to the total appearance and the sequel to the helicopters. This applies especially to the overall picture because Ezekiel explicitly compares this with what he had seen by the Chebar River. Throughout this chapter the helicopters are called cherubim, which justifies our speaking of helicopters in the plural (plural form: -im). On the other hand the use of the term "living creature" is confusing when it relates to the vehicle, since Ezekiel used it earlier to identify the helicopters. However, since Ezekiel stresses the identity with the spaceships he had observed earlier, this ambiguity has no technical significance.

11:1. The spirit lifted me up, and brought me to the east gate of the house of the Lord, which faces east; . . .

11:2. And he said to me: "Son of man, these are . . ."

11:22. Then the cherubim lifted up their wings, with the wheels beside them; and the glory of the God of Israel was over them.

11:23. And the glory of the Lord went up from the midst of the city, and stood upon the mountain which is on the east side of the city.

11:24. And the spirit lifted me up and brought me in the vision of God by the spirit into Chaldea, to the exiles. Then the vision I had seen went up from me.

Verse 1: The commentary of Reference 6, page 56, identifies the "east gate" to which Ezekiel is now brought as the gate of the outer court. We know from Chapter 10, Verse 19, that a short while earlier the commander too had flown there with his spaceship. The beginning of this verse includes a phrase which is often repeated: "The spirit lifted me up, and brought me . . ." It comes up whenever Ezekiel either boards the spaceship or experiences a change in his location other than by walking. We shall return later to the analysis of this expression.

Verse 2: Since now both Ezekiel and the commander are at the east gate, it is no surprise to read that the commander speaks again to Ezekiel. It is noteworthy, however, that Verses 22 to 24 rule out the presence of Ezekiel in the capsule. The commander must therefore have left it again and necessarily must have returned to it before takeoff. The absence of any corresponding text must unfortunately lead to the conclusion that only a fragment came down to us with the beginning of Chapter 11. The missing part is not of essential significance to either the prophetic or the technical aspect of Ezekiel's report, yet it would no doubt have been of considerable technical interest.

Verse 22: We are witnessing activity immediately preceding the flight. With the start of the rotor, the blades that were hanging downward are "lifted up"; they begin to develop lift and the whole vehicle—crowned by the glittering capsule of the commander—rolls a short distance from its location. Ezekiel registers the picture in his memory with almost photographic sharpness.

Verse 23: Then follows the takeoff, the ascent, and eventually the horizontal flight to the "mountain which is on the east side of the city."

These two Verses are of unusual value: They constitute an eyewitness report by an onlooker! Somebody is speaking to us, who has observed the whole procedure from the outside. These few sentences give documentary evidence of something extraordinary: A man describes the takeoff and terrestrial flight of a spacecraft, without excitement, in sober, matter-of-fact words, 2500 years before our time!

Something else is striking in this report, namely, the avoidance of the name which—according to the commentators—is borne by this mountain: the Mount of Olives.

Verse 24: At the beginning we encounter again two already well-known expressions ("the spirit" and "in the vision of God") which tell us that Ezekiel boards a spaceship and flies in it. Since he had been flown here, he must have been brought back by air too, so that the fact that he is taking this flight is no surprise. Yet it quickly assumes significance as we realize that the vehicle that was the focus of attention throughout this third encounter has just left. Besides, the final Verses of this Chapter inform us that Ezekiel is *not* flying home in the same spaceship in which he came. This situation leads to the conclusion of the presence of a second spacecraft. Such a conclusion cannot really surprise; it was pointed out earlier that the deployment of a single vehicle —which moreover seems to be concerned exclusively with Ezekiel—is too illogical and uneconomical to be credible.

As we ponder over the events that took place here and of which we can perceive only a dim outline, we come to regard the presence of a second spaceship as quite justified. There are several indications that the removal of a "hot" part was of a critical nature (Chapter 10, Verse 7). A second spacecraft was therefore very desirable. The commander of the first could reach it, if necessary, with the aid of his capsule; after all, he did summon the capsule to his side. That second spaceship must have been at a safe distance from the scene of the critical procedure, so as not to be damaged in case of an accident. Therefore Ezekiel *could* not have seen it earlier.

In addition, the availability of the second spaceship easily resolves the "transportation problem" of Ezekiel in Verse 1: Since the critical moment had passed, the commander could leave his spaceship and take Ezekiel to the east gate. In the course of the next encounter we shall be confronted with several short flights of this kind, at which time we shall discuss them in more detail.

The fourth encounter

40:1. In the twenty-fifth year of our exile, at the beginning of the year, on the tenth day of the month, in the fourteenth year after the city was conquered, on that very day, the hand of the Lord was upon me,

40:2. and he brought me in the visions of God into the land of Israel, and set me down upon a very high mountain, on which was a structure like a city opposite me.

40:3. When he brought me there, behold, there was a man, whose appearance was like bronze, with a line of flax and a measuring reed in his hand; and he was standing in the gateway.

40:4. And the man said to me: "Son of man, look with your eyes and hear with your ears, and set your mind upon all that I shall show you, for you were brought here in order that I might show it to you; declare all that you see to the house of Israel."

Verse 1: Some nineteen years elapse before Ezekiel feels again the "hand of the Lord."

Verse 2: Without going into any details, he mentions his flight "in the visions of God" to a "very high mountain." He alights outside a number of buildings, and the general impression they convey is described by him as one of a "structure like a city." He is again totally unimpressed; the commander is simply referred to as "he."

Verse 3: Ezekiel's arrival had obviously been arranged, because "behold, there was a man." Ezekiel in no way indicates that he has ever seen man or commander before.

Ezekiel's familiarity with the spaceship and the commander prompts him to omit their so often repeated description. That "man" on the contrary is new to him, so he does describe him. There is no doubt that he indeed beholds a man and not some new different form of vehicle because, in contrast to his earlier descriptions, he is now talking about a "hand" and no longer about the "form of a hand" (compare Chapter 8, Verse 3). Moreover, this same man accompanies him and guides him through the temple. He is wearing a metallic or metallike suit. The various translations mention—apart from the word "bronze"—such terms as brass and metal. However, all these definitions have in common the impression of a metallic surface.

The nature of this suit may be ascertained with sufficient assurance on the basis of the following considerations. At the time of this encounter Ezekiel was probably about fifty years old and no doubt had seen on many occasions coats of mail and suits of plated armor as worn by the warriors of his time. We are now sufficiently familiar with his gift of observation to say that he would certainly have adequately described any man wearing such armor. On the other hand, there is a certain degree of similarity here with his description of the appearance of the commander during the first and third encounters; the only missing point is a mention of the brightness observed on those occasions. The latter fact, however, loses significance because this time Ezekiel is obviously not interested at all in describing any attending circum-

stances. At the beginning of the encounter, the spaceship
is not described at all and later only by a comparison
with earlier encounters; the temple, on the other hand,
is described with an enormous amount of detail. We can
therefore be almost certain that this very general depiction indicates a protective suit of the kind worn by the
commander.

The man carries a "line of flax" and a "measuring
reed" in his hand. As we learn from Verse 5 of this
Chapter, this measuring reed is "six cubits long, each
being a cubit and a handbreadth in length." According
to Reference 6, page 267, this corresponds to a length
of 10½ feet. Although the measuring reed seems to
have been used during the subsequent walk through the
large temple, both these items—the measuring reed and
the line of flax—would certainly be of interest to engineers specialized in communications and related fields.

Verse 4: The man strongly enjoins Ezekiel to remember everything that he is about to see and then to describe
it accurately to the people of Israel. Again a phrase
occurs here surprisingly "human" in its context: ". . . you
were brought here in order that I might show it to you."

43:1. Afterward he brought me to the gate, the gate
facing east.

43:2. And behold, the glory of the God of Israel came
from the east; and the sound of his coming was
like the sound of many waters; and the earth shone
with his glory.

Verse 2: It is only in Reference 5 that the new arrival
of a spaceship is described with the use of the expression
"broke in from the east"; all other translations consulted
here say that it "came." The former version might be
understood in the sense of the first encounter, that is of
a landing initiated by the rocket engine.

What really happened here, however, can be quite
easily reconstructed: at his arrival on the "very high
mountain" (Chapter 40, Verse 2) Ezekiel was put down
at some distance from a gate which is later identified as
the east gate. He leaves the spacecraft which therefore
was also standing outside the east gate, and proceeds

with the man to undertake an extensive walking tour through the temple. Now the spaceship takes off from its location outside the gate and flies in a straight line to the temple building in the inner court. Accordingly, if observed from the outer court, it must necessarily be coming from the east. The fact that it is really the whole spacecraft that is flying over Ezekiel with the aid of its helicopters is evidenced by the comparison made in the text with the "sound of many waters." The same description: "the sound of many waters," is used in Chapter 1, Verse 24, in connection with the sound and noise of the helicopters. For the time being there is no satisfactory explanation for the light effect.

> **43:3.** And the vision I saw was like the vision which I had seen when he came to destroy the city. And the vehicular structure I saw was like the vision which I had seen by the river Chebar; and I fell upon my face.

Verse 3: These few lines contain remarkable details. First of all Ezekiel confirms that this spaceship looked exactly like the one of the third encounter (". . . came to destroy the city"). At that time, on the other hand, he had also acknowledged the identity with the spaceships of earlier encounters. The introductory passage of this Verse shows therefore that over a span of twenty years Ezekiel always saw the same type of spacecraft!

The retention of a configuration over such a long period of time, however, is possible only when its design has matured. Such a situation requires a commensurate level in many fields and is therefore possible only after an appropriately long development period. At no earlier stage is a static condition possible. We ourselves, for example, are still too much at the beginning of a technical era to be *other than dynamic*. The structures and methods we develop are therefore in constant flux; it is only in the area of the simplest devices and tools that we have achieved a status where changes are slow or nonexistent. In the area of "machines," continuous development of engineering and technology determines equally continuous changes in our products. The few exceptions are found in small aircraft and the Volkswagen. What has happened in these two cases is applicable also to the spaceships seen by Ezekiel: For a specific purpose and within the framework of a given technology an optimal, a "definitive" form has been found. From this point on, true progress can only occur through something like a mutation.

From our somewhat limited point of view the spacecraft described by Ezekiel appears to belong to the class of such fully matured products: So long as no means other than helicopters were available for the terrestrial flight and pertinent requirements, substantial changes in the spaceship were impossible. A mutation which might have led to new forms and functions did not take place during the period of observation.

There is a second way of looking at it—which would completely overthrow all the arguments set forth above, however—namely, the assumption that spaceship and crew belonged to a different dimension of time. However, in view of the presence of humanlike beings and of the surprisingly small difference between the technology that had made that spaceship possible and our own technology, this thought does not appear to me to have enough merit to deserve serious consideration.

One also notices that in Verse 3 Ezekiel makes comparisons with the spacecraft of the first and third encounters and never mentions the second. On the other hand, he does explicitly compare the spaceship of the third encounter with the one he had seen during the second. (Compare Chapter 8, Verse 4, with Chapter 3, Verse 22 and 23.) An explanation for the omission of the second encounter may be found in the fact that, at that time, the spaceship was obviously of secondary significance while in the two other cases it was clearly at the very center of interest and action.

Finally, attention is drawn also to a difference in the texts. As was the case in the second Verse, so here too the translation given in Reference 5 is markedly different from all the others. As a typical example of the content of these other translations, Reference 3 is quoted here. It reads:

43:3. And the vision I saw was like the vision which I had seen when he came to destroy the city, and like the vision which I had seen by the river Chebar; and I fell on my face.

We see that both versions confirm the identity of the vehicles. But Reference 5 has an interesting insert which mentions "the vehicular structure" and which can probably be traced back to different original texts. This expression is of much interest to us insofar as the spaceship was evidently so described because of its wheels, which provides a further confirmation of its identity.

43:4. As the glory of the Lord entered the temple over the gate facing east,

43:5. . . . a spirit lifted me up, and brought me into the inner court; and behold, the glory of the Lord filled the temple.

43:6. While the man was standing beside me, I heard one speaking to me from the temple;

43:7. . . . and he said to me: "Son of man, this is the place of my throne and the place of the soles of my feet, where I will dwell in the midst of the people of Israel forever. . . ."

Verse 4: The vehicle which flew in, on its helicopters, from the east, proceeds to land beside the temple and in so doing arrives "over the gate" that faces the east. This word "over" has been rendered, in all English translations consulted, by the word "by," which can also have the meaning of "over." References 1 and 2 alone translate it as "through." Consistently with the action, "over" or "by" (provided the latter is interpreted as having the same meaning) are doubtless the right words. Although this point as such may not be of real significance, a clarification of the contents of the original texts would be quite interesting.

Verse 5: Ezekiel is taken to the inner court. He does not say—as he did elsewhere—"he led me" or "he made me go," but specifically "brought me." At the outset of this encounter we saw that the "man" is most probably clad in a suit similar to that of the commander. He may therefore also have been equipped with that small propulsive device that makes individual flying possible (compare p. 42). In such a case he is, of course, able to lift Ezekiel into the air and to carry him over a moderate distance. The text clearly describes this procedure: ". . . lifted me up, and brought me . . ." It should be repeated at this point that devices and procedures of this kind are in no way unrealistic from a technical point of view. If anything, it is probably rather astonishing that such devices have not been developed much further in our time. Their evident advantages in overcoming short or moderate distances (for example, on large construction sites) and the attraction they may have for sportsmen will probably enhance interest in such devices in the not too distant future.

Verse 6: We again witness Ezekiel's ability to make precise distinctions. As in most cases, he bestows upon the majestic spectacle of the flying spaceship an appropriately impressive characterization—"the glory of the Lord" (Verse 5). However, it does not escape his especially critical observation that the voice coming from there is perfectly real and, as it were, terrestrial. Instead of saying, as one would expect, "the voice of the Lord," he very soberly says ". . . I heard one speaking to me from the temple."

This Verse gives a very clear picture of the situation: Ezekiel and the man who has just brought him over the wall are standing in the court; and the commander, who has also just landed, speaks to him. The speech is coming "from the temple," that is, over some distance, and this leads to the conclusion that a loudspeaker was used, which was already used to summon the ground crew during the third encounter (Chapter 9, Verse 1).

This scene fully eliminates any suspicion that may have been harbored to the effect that the commander and the man were the same person. Moreover it strongly conveys the impression that the "man" did look like a human being.

Verse 7: The text indicates with some degree of certainty that it is the commander who speaks to Ezekiel.

Yet the latter omits any particularly respectful terms and refers to the speaker simply as "he."

44:1. Then he brought me back to the outer gate of the sanctuary, which faces east; and it was shut.

44:4. Then he brought me by way of the north gate to the front of the temple; and I looked, and behold, the glory of the Lord filled the temple of the Lord; and I fell upon my face.

Verses 1 and 4: For the first and only time "he brought" Ezekiel from one place to another. "He" is not in this case the "spirit" usually referred to. "He" is this time the man who leads him. Thus, literally at the very last moment, Verse 4 hands us the key to the clarification of the so often used words "he brought."

This clarification begins with the determination of the itinerary, which establishes that Ezekiel was brought from the east gate to the temple via the north gate—which means a detour. If we first assume that Ezekiel and his leader *walked* this route, we must consult the plan of the temple. It is probably not possible to draw a plan entirely consistent with all the available information. Nonetheless, the basic pattern and arrangements of the courts can be reconstructed with sufficient certainty from the texts (Chapters 42 to 44).

The plan thus obtained shows us that the route as described was not possible at all. There is no connection between the eastern and the northern courts. To be able to *walk* as described, from the outer east gate through the north gate to the temple, the two would have had to leave the temple grounds through the outer east gate, walk along its outer perimeter first in the northern and then in the western direction, and finally pass through the outer north gate, the outer court, the inner north gate, and the inner court, to arrive at the temple. A weighty circumstance rules out this long march as a possibility: The outer east gate is locked! (Verse 1.)

If, on the other hand, Ezekiel and the man who accompanied him were to go directly to the temple, they would have had to pass through the *east gate* of the inner court. Thus, only one answer is left: The described itinerary is possible *only by air*.

Upon arrival before the temple, Ezekiel finds the commander and the spaceship still present and Ezekiel falls prostrate.

Thus ends the fourth and last encounter insofar as the description of the spacecraft, its commander, and the ground crew is concerned.

6

COMPLEMENTS AND INSIGHTS

THE foregoing part of the book presented detailed comparisons of the Biblical text with the technical exposition and established their concordance. In this and the next sections of the book a summary is given of specific characteristics and features which are scattered over large portions of Ezekiel's report. This method of argumentation contributes to deeper understanding and is therefore a part of the evidence. It also leads to new and surprising consequences which, although they are not of a technical nature, are directly dependent on the technical study and thus are also part of this investigation.

Leitmotifs

Three expressions are consistently used in Ezekiel's book to indicate certain conditions or events. The occurrences of these expressions are too typical and too clearly linked to certain phases of the events to be regarded as merely coincidental.

We come across the first of these expressions at the outset of each encounter. It is so conspicuously placed that—to continue musical comparisons—it can be truly described as an upbeat. This is how it reads:

First encounter   1:3. The hand of the Lord was upon him there.

Second encounter	3:22. And the hand of the Lord was there upon me.
Third encounter	8:1. The hand of the Lord God fell there upon me.
Fourth encounter	40:1. The hand of the Lord was upon me.

This rule is broken only in one instance at the beginning of the flight during the first encounter when Ezekiel is overcome by shock and says, in Chapter 3:

3:14. . . . and I went in bitterness in the heat of my spirit, the hand of the Lord being strong upon me.

The content of this last verse could perhaps include the key to the explanation of the "hand of the Lord" because, as already mentioned earlier, it might be regarded as a hint of a hypnotic influence.

The investigation of the actual meaning of this expression does not belong among the objectives of this book. Its mention is nevertheless necessary because it occurs exclusively in encounters with the spacecraft. By way of contrast, all visions are introduced by the words: "the word of the Lord came to me . . ." or similar formulas with minor alterations. This evident differentiation is also pointed out in Reference 6, page 41. It is given so much emphasis that its intentional character cannot be misunderstood. We shall come back to this aspect in section 7.

The second expression is "Then the spirit lifted me up" or "the spirit took hold of me" or similar formulas with minor variations. In each case this expression indicates an actual lifting. Immediately thereafter Ezekiel either flies or makes a short "leap." While no doubt is possible with regard to the action itself, the uncertainty remains unabated regarding the word "spirit." Two departures from the standard version are significant in this connection. One relates to the obvious discrepancy between Chapter 43 on the one hand and Chapter 44 on the other:

| Standard version | 43:5. . . . a spirit lifted me up, and brought me . . . |

Discrepant versions   44:1. Then he brought me . . .
                        44:4. Then brought he me . . .

Since in the last two verses "he" refers to the accompanying man it becomes easy to identify the "spirit" with that "man" in Chapter 43, Verse 5, and also in Chapter 11, Verse 1. Such a solution is entirely consistent with the actual possibilities and expectations as already discussed earlier. In Reference 6, page 301, an analogous view is put forward when "he" is interpreted as referring to the accompanying angel: "The subject of the verb is the angel who acted as a guide."

The second deviation, however, creates some difficulties with this interpretation. It occurs only in References 1 and 2 which use the word "wind" every time instead of the word "spirit." If we accept the thus suggested possibility that the expression is ambiguous in the original text, then the word "wind" can be read two ways. On the one hand it can mean in a direct sense the movement of air caused by the operation of the small nozzles. On the other hand, it allows yet another fundamentally new possibility, the elucidation of which requires a reference to Chapter 8, where Ezekiel reports:

8:3. He put forth the form of a hand, and took me by the lock of my head; and the spirit lifted me up . . .

Let us consider the sequence of this scene as it is depicted. The mechanical arm moves its hand toward Ezekiel, holds it over his head, and Ezekiel has a feeling as though the hand grips him by the hair. Then a spirit (a wind) lifts him up.

First it must be noted that Ezekiel clearly distinguishes between two actions: the touching of his hair and his upward movement. He allows no doubt of the fact that he was lifted by a "spirit" and not by his hair!

The possibility of substituting "wind" for "spirit" opens up remarkable prospects.

A charge of static electricity results in the hair standing up. We also know that a strong field of static electricity produces a movement of air, actually a wind! Surely, Ezekiel is not lifted up by the wind itself. But the wind could be the product of an electrical field and as such an indication of a means of lifting and moving of which we know very little today.

Now, whether the "hand" really touched Ezekiel's hair or whether the bristling of hair he felt was a result of a static charge, is a detail of secondary importance. Anyhow, we have again encountered an occurrence deserving a closer study by specialists.

We conclude, therefore, that this second expression definitely means a lifting process, and that merely the lifting device employed for that purpose might be different from what was postulated so far.

The third leitmotif always means Ezekiel's flight in the spacecraft. It reads as follows:

8:3. . . . brought me in visions of God . . .
11:24. . . . brought me in the vision of God . . .
40:2. . . . brought me in the visions of God . . .

To explain the identification of a flight with "visions of God," we have only to consider a little more closely the experience of flying. For most people of our time flying, and particularly the first flight, is a wonderful experience; and this is so despite the fact that flying as a possibility is of course known to them. There is no doubt that after he recovered from the shock of the first encounter Ezekiel must have been fascinated with the view of the earth seen from above. To round off the argument, let us not forget that God at that time—(and often still today)—was supposed to dwell in the heavens, that is, "above." Therefore Ezekiel saw the earth during his flight as God must be seeing it: he saw it "in the visions of God"! Whether he coined and transmitted this expression himself or whether it was perhaps chosen by a subsequent writer of his book to convey the quintessence of a description he could not understand is beside the point.

A clear departure from this mode of expression is found in Ezekiel's first flight:

3:14. I went in bitterness in the heat of my spirit.

We still recall the shock into which he lapsed under

the overwhelming impact of the first encounter. Truly, he did fly, but "the heat" of his spirit very understandably spoiled any enjoyment of this flight. He does not look down to the earth and therefore, during this flight and this flight alone, he does not experience "visions of God."

The temples

In the third encounter

This encounter takes place approximately one year after the first one, which means about 591 B.C. At the outset we learn from Verse 3 of Chapter 8 that Ezekiel was flown to the temple of Jerusalem. As the story unfolds, temple courts or their gates are mentioned four times in the following verses and their site descriptions:

Chapter 8, Verse 3: gateway of the inner court
Chapter 10, Verse 5: outer court
Chapter 10, Verse 19: east gate of the temple
Chapter 11, Verse 1: east gate of the temple

The majority of translations and commentators consulted agree with the above descriptions. With regard to Chapter 10, Verse 19, and Chapter 11, Verse 1, where none of the translations contains a detailed description of the site, the commentator in Reference 6 shows that the first verse speaks of the inner court, while the latter verse means the outer court (Reference 6, pp. 55, 56).

From the history of the temple we know that it was destroyed in 586 B.C., that is, five years after the event discussed here. According to the text, Ezekiel was landed in the temple of Solomon. It is therefore quite interesting that Solomon's temple—as a glimpse at the map (Reference 4, p. 1311) will show—had only *one* wall and no outer courts! This is explicitly acknowledged in Reference 4, p. 619, under letter K; it reads: "Solomon's temple had no outer court and was separated from his palace only by the single wall of the inner court."

This surprising development is underscored by a discrepancy in the description of the terrain. In Chapter 9, Verse 2, we read that the "men came from the direction of the upper gate." The above-mentioned map, on the other hand, shows the building of the temple on a hill; the north gate of the temple of Solomon was therefore situated *lower*. In this context it is relevant to quote Reference 6, page 47, which contains the following commentary: "This may be identical with the gate built by King Jotham. It was situated in the north-east and received its name because it stood higher than the rest of the temple court." Thus the problem of the terrain is balanced, in a way, by a counterstatement; but now we are confronted with the question of the *direction* in which that gate lies. The commentator, moreover, seems uncertain, because he writes: "This may be," so that, in the final analysis, the location of the gate still remains in doubt.

Finally, this group of questions also includes the remarkable passage in Chapter 11, Verse 23, which says that the landing took place "upon the mountain which is on the east side of the city." Someone who knew Jerusalem as well as Ezekiel did would not only as a matter of course know the name of that mountain—the Mount of Olives—but would certainly have used this familiar name in an equally matter-of-fact way had he really wanted to refer to that mountain, especially in speaking to people who like himself were perfectly familiar with the area. We remember in this connection that Ezekiel never fails to mention his community of exiles "by the river Chebar."

As a preliminary summary we can therefore establish that the description of the temple does not agree with the temple of Solomon in Jerusalem and also that a mountain is identified not by its name but by its location.

We take the first step toward a clarification of this confusing situation by trusting Ezekiel's often proven gift of observation and lucidity of mind—in other words, we accept his description as accurate and correct. The conclusion which naturally follows therefrom precisely coincides with what he says: he was in a temple and he did see a mountain, but the temple was not in Jerusalem and therefore the mountain was not the Mount of Olives. For the second step we use the view developed and substantiated in the next section of this book, namely that Ezekiel's book in the form which has come down to us was not written by him. At the time it was written, the temple of Solomon had been destroyed for decades. The return of the Jews from the Babylonian exile began in the year 538 B.C., that is, fifty-nine years after their deportation. The probability that at that time anyone was still alive who had seen Solomon's temple and knew it from personal observation is extremely low. An editor of Ezekiel's book could therefore in good faith and with the best intentions have seen the temple of this encounter in the general religious context and could have placed it in Jerusalem.

These are the first steps of perhaps many which may have to be taken; because the answer has not yet been found to the question where Ezekiel really had been.

In the fourth encounter

If we neglect—without giving any reasons for the time being—the references to Jerusalem and Israel in the two introductory verses, we will find the only, and vague, information concerning the location of the temple in the description given in Chapter 40, Verse 2: "upon a very high mountain." The temple, including its measurements, is described in incredible detail and turns out to be a very large complex. Reading the text, one has the impression that on the basis of this information—because of the abundance of details—it would be easy to draw a plan of the temple. This impression vanishes quickly when one tries to actually do it; and there are points on which even Bible commentators disagree. The temple complex as a vision is an object of contention because the temple was never built, and when the temple in Jerusalem was rebuilt, there was not even an attempt to build it according to the plan outlined in the Book of Ezekiel (Reference 4, p. 617, letter A; Reference 5, p. 1056).

The temple covers a square with a side length of over 350 feet. The very size of the complex reduces the credibility of its location on a high mountain. A further argument along the same lines is the description of the river in Chapter 47. This river begins as a small brook which emerges from under the southern part of the eastern temple wall and flows eastward. The brook becomes a river farther to the east and flows between fertile banks. This description suddenly ends with Verse 12; from Verse 13 to the end of the next Chapter (which is also the end of the book) we find the contents of a vision. The separation of the first twelve verses from the rest is unmistakable.

This separation is evidenced by the sudden change of theme and also a change of style which, without any transition, passes from the form of a narrative to that of an injunction. Moreover, Verse 13 starts with a new introduction: "Thus says the Lord God. . . ." The description of the river must therefore be counted as part of the temple description, and it rules out its location at the indicated site.

A third argument against the "mountain" is Ezekiel's first impression after the landing which he describes in the following words:

> **40:2.** and brought me in the visions of God into the land of Israel, and set me down upon a very high mountain, on which was a structure like a city opposite me.

It would seem extremely unlikely for an outstanding observer such as Ezekiel to take a city for a temple complex and vice versa. Even more so since the temple is a vast and majestic structure so that no such confusion is possible even when reading the report. Later Ezekiel does describe the temple but not the city. His report on this encounter ends abruptly, without any visible reason; and the end of it is also the end of the book. The traditional text is therefore unmistakably a fragment. A mention of the return flight is missing; and if the city is not mentioned or discussed again, this also must be attributed to the same reason.

Besides, the presence of a city would be a necessary conclusion even if it were not mentioned at all: The need for such a huge temple complex can only arise in the vicinity of a large settlement. These considerations too supply good reason to assume buildings outside the temple, and to eliminate the mountain as a site.

So we see a large temple complex, the city belonging to it, and a stream flowing eastward and developing into a river. The "mountain" thus loses its form and is replaced by a vast landscape. Ezekiel could perhaps have seen "a very high mountain" while flying toward it; but with our elimination of this landmark he also loses the ability of a *visual* determination of a high altitude. The latter now only becomes noticeable through a more or less acute difficulty in breathing and the slowness of all movements due to the rarefied air.

Where had Ezekiel really been?

7

TEXT, AUTHOR, AND REPORT

So far we have discussed in great detail the relationships between Ezekiel's book and its underlying technical conditions. We now want to proceed to a treatment of the report as a whole in the light of the knowledge we have acquired. In the course of our investigation we have come across peculiarities in the text structure of those parts of the report which were the object of our scrutiny. They can be classified in three categories: localized confusion, incompleteness, and unmotivated changes of theme. The last category is probably a direct result of the other two. However, within the framework of this book we are not interested in clarifying this particular point, but rather in the consequences and questions arising out of the existence of these peculiarities. Therefore we can confine ourselves simply to pointing out their existence, which we will do by mentioning relevant examples only. In so doing, we will notice that some of these discrepancies can come to light only through our disclosure of the actual events.

From this point of view the most striking feature of the book are those passages where the order of presentation is very confused, many of which will be apparent to even a casual reader. Sentences, verses, and repetitions occur variously without any correlation with either the preceding or the following parts of the text. We come across such inserts already in the first Chapter. For example, let us look at the following passage:

1:8. Under their wings on their four sides they had human hands. And the four had their faces and their wings thus:

1:9. Their wings touched one another; they went every one straight forward, without turning as they went.

1:10. As for the likeness of their faces, each had the face of a man in front; the four had the face of a lion on the right side, the four had the face of a bull on the left side, and the four had the face of an eagle at the back.

The second part of Verse 8 and the whole of Verse 9 are undeniably at the wrong place here, and they interrupt the continuity of the description. On the other hand, Verse 9 itself is again subdivided. Let us consider its second passage which reads:

1:9. . . . they went every one straight forward, without turning as they went.

The same statement is suddenly repeated in Verses 12 and 17:

1:12. And each went straight forward; wherever the spirit would make them go, they went, without turning as they went.

1:17. When they went, they went in any of their four directions without turning as they went.

And finally it occurs again in Verses 19 to 21 of the same Chapter 1.

But the most extended confusion of the text is encountered in Chapter 10. Here not only the basic action becomes mixed with structural descriptions, but the technical descriptions themselves are again incoherent, uneven, and repetitive. The high degree of lack of continuity in the text structure can best be illustrated by the following graph indicating the numbers of the verses in juxtaposition with their contents. The table shows us the following picture:

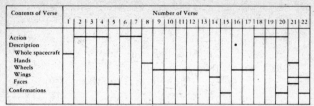

Juxtaposition of Verse Number and Contents

We find that the progress and the continuity of the action developed in Chapter 10 is interrupted already in the first Verse, which, as was shown in section 4 of this book, really belongs in Chapter 9. The specific action of Chapter 10 thus begins in Verse 2. It is soon interrupted again by Verse 5, then briefly continued in Verses 6 and 7, to be completely banished for a long spell by the technical details of Verses 8 to 17. It is not picked up again until almost the end of the Chapter (Verses 18 and 19); and Verse 20, containing as it does an explicit and therefore relevant confirmation, may possibly also be regarded as pertaining to the action. Verses 21 and 22 are additions which again contain confirmation but are entirely misplaced at this point.

The technical descriptions that interrupt the action are in accord with those given in Chapter 1, to such a degree that some parts are word for word identical; the only exceptions are Verses 12 and 14. The former concerns the distribution of "eyes" over the whole vehicle and has already been discussed at length. The faces mentioned in Verse 14 have also been investigated with respect to their actual appearance. It should only be added here that in this case Ezekiel sees a different face turned toward him than the one in Chapter 1. This is no surprise, since Ezekiel's own position with reference to the spaceship may have been different.

Among the examples of incomplete text one could conceivably include the description of the command capsule in Verses 26 to 28 of Chapter 1. However, in view of the general difficulty of describing it, as discussed in section 4 above, such inclusion is question-

able. The second encounter, on the contrary, can clearly
be recognized as a fragment because, while it begins in
Chapter 3, Verse 22, it is never brought to a conclusion. Even the beginning itself is incomplete because, in
contrast to all the other encounters, there is no information regarding the date.

Another example will be found at the beginning of the
third encounter. In Verses 2 and 3 of Chapter 8 fragments have been combined, the meaning and correlation
of which can be understood only on the basis of the description provided on the occasion of the first encounter.
The suspicion that in this case Ezekiel sees something
that is different from what he saw during the earlier and
later encounters is eliminated by Chapter 43, Verse 3,
which explicitly identifies the spacecraft of the fourth
encounter with that of the first and third.

> **43:3.** And the vision I saw was like the vision which
> I had seen when he came to destroy the city. And
> the vehicular structure I saw was like the vision
> which I had seen by the river Chebar; and I fell
> upon my face.

In this verse "to destroy the city" means the third encounter and "which I had seen by the river Chebar"
the first. The same reference to the first encounter is also
found in the introduction to the second (Chapter 3,
Verse 23). All these pronounced references confirm the
identity of the spaceships observed and we can therefore all the more surely characterize Verses 2 and 3 of
Chapter 8—which are under discussion here—as fragments.

With regard to the fourth encounter, we have already
discussed the two groups of features which lead us to
recognize that its description is incomplete: the story
of that encounter comes to an abrupt end without any
statements about Ezekiel's return to his community,
such as he had made in the first and third encounters;
also, there are no further comments on the city seen by
Ezekiel at the outset.

The sudden beginning of the story of the second encounter is a good example of an abrupt change of topic.

It is understandable only if one recognizes the already mentioned absence of date. Earlier we scrutinized from another angle a drastic change of theme in the narration of the fourth encounter. It concerns the sudden transition from description to injunction in Verses 12 and 13 of Chapter 47. Here again it is quite possible that his "jump" from one line of thought to another is due to missing text.

Finally, in this context, it is appropriate to discuss— if only briefly—a special case not mentioned so far. It concerns the location of beginning and end of the first encounter. We read:

> **1:1.** . . . . as I was among the exiles by the river Chebar . . .

But it is also a remarkable fact that, at the end of this encounter, Ezekiel flies to that very same community:

> **3:15.** And I came to the exiles at Tel-Abib . . .

If we take these statements literally, they mean that both the beginning and the end of this flight occurred in the immediate vicinity of the same place. In other words: the commander took Ezekiel on a local flight. In section 8 of this book we shall see that this is, in fact, less absurd than one might at first think. The other possible interpretation would be to assume gross negligence on the part of the writer of that report, which— for this very reason—would appear unlikely. It should be pointed out that neither Reference 4 nor Reference 6 offers any comments on this point.

In conclusion we can say that the text-related problems discussed here are, fortunately, only sporadic. It is true that here and there they may make the understanding somewhat more difficult, but their import falls far below a level where they could seriously impede the correct interpretation. Their real significance is therefore limited to the following considerations which concern the author.

All these quite noticeable discrepancies in the text become much more striking as we reflect that they are supposed to be the work of a man gifted with exceptional lucidity of mind and powers of observation. The longer one ponders this contradiction, the less one is inclined to believe that a man capable of registering and describing such stunning experiences with such accuracy would then be unable to present his report in a coherent fashion. The tension between these two poles is too powerful not to produce the feeling of a separation between observer and author, and thus generating the desire for an explanation.

Before we can contemplate and possibly accept such a separation of identities, we have to ask ourselves whether Ezekiel could yet be the author of the report which has come down to us. As has already been said, he was about fifty years old at the time of the fourth and last encounter and could thus have recorded his experiences in writing when he was in his sixties. The discrepancies might then be construed as the result of a weakening of his intellectual faculties because of his age. Such a view, however, is in no way acceptable. Suffice it to point to the precision of his descriptions and also to the absence of any contradictions within these descriptions and with respect to the technical reconstruction. In that regard there is not the slightest hint of a dimming of the intellect and therefore it would be illogical to assume it with respect to the simpler task of mere writing. Therefore we can with full assurance eliminate Ezekiel as the direct writer of the book which has come down to us.

The question of what actually happened receives a simple answer in that we again take Ezekiel at his word. He says: ". . . I spoke to the exiles . . ."; that means he reported his experiences and visions orally. One or more people among his audience may have put these reports in writing in a more or less detailed form. Ezekiel himself may have made notes. After his death and perhaps even after the end of the exile, that material was edited by someone in the form of a book. We are deeply indebted to that anonymous author. Without his painstaking labor we would have no knowledge of Ezekiel's revealing encounters.

It is however quite understandable if this author had had an inner rapport with only the visionary part of the story. Information concerning encounters with alien and huge flying objects could not have had any real significance for him and—because of their incomprehensible nature—could be used and adduced by him merely as a component of visions. It is remarkable that such fusion is reduced to a minimum. In general, the author has included technical passages in closed groups among the visions. Thanks to this not only were the technical descriptions preserved for us in such magnificent form but so also were Ezekiel's own reactions to what he saw. Just let us think how easy it would have been for that author—and how natural it actually was for him—to change the passages he could not understand, for example, the one where the commander is referred to as man (Adam) or identified as "he"! But the author was endowed with enough admirable integrity and truthfulness to avoid impressing his personal attitude on what he received. He subordinated himself to his task in the best sense of the word and in so doing gave us a truly extraordinary work.

This dedicated truthfulness commands our understanding of the instances where various fragments were not correctly put together. The author may have found them individually, isolated, or he may have had several descriptions of the same part of the spacecraft. His natural absence of knowledge of the real structure prevented him from seeing the relationships, so that he had neither a reason for nor indeed the possibility of following an order of arrangement which we, today, know to be the correct one. Occasional incompleteness and sudden theme changes are also understandable: it is of course possible, indeed probable, that the oral and written information accessible to the author was not complete. It probably came from many sources, and death as well as other accidents of life left gaps in the available material. The author's attitude was upheld anew; in such circumstances he added nothing, he did not round off any corners. He allows the report to speak to us in the form in which it was transmitted to him.

The very few places where he departs from this attitude have only been briefly mentioned in this study. Presently we shall see that for most of these cases there is a valid explanation.

The first time such a spot is encountered is in Chapter 1, Verse 14, which mentions the swift back and forth movement of the spacecraft, the speed of which is compared to that of lightning.

In the discussion of Verse 4 of Chapter 9 it was pointed out there, for the first and only time, the commander is referred to as "the Lord." But the commander has already been clearly identified as "man" (Adam) on an earlier occasion. The new identification used here can therefore only be regarded as an error.

It is also appropriate to comment here on the seemingly very smooth connection between vision and technical happenings during the third encounter (Chapters 8, 9, and 11). To some extent, reference thereto has already been made in section 5. A very remarkable factor, however, was not discussed there because it did not pertain to the sequence of events as such: in Verse 11 of Chapter 9 the man clad in linen reports that he has carried out the order. The order was to kill all those guilty of abominations. In Verse 8, Chapter 9, Ezekiel himself confirms with anguish that "I was left alone." In Verses 1 and 2 of Chapter 11, however, we read to our surprise:

11:1. . . . and behold at the door of the gateway there were twenty-five men; and I saw among them Jaazaniah, the son of Azzur, and Pelatiah, the son of Benaiah, princes of the people.

11:2. And he said to me: "Son of man, these are the men that devise iniquity, and who give wicked counsel in this city."

So, contrary to all earlier statements, we see here a group of men who are explicitly described as some of the "wicked." They are not only alive but not a word is wasted to comment on their presence. The obvious contradiction between this scene and the preceding ones forces us to assume that both episodes were put here instead of other statements made by the commander, which could not be understood by the author. The suspenseful third encounter gives sufficient grounds for pertinent assumptions.

Finally, two more cases deserve to be mentioned: the use of the words "visions of God" and the sites of the temples. They were sufficiently discussed in section 6 of this book so that no further comments are necessary and we can therefore confine ourselves to merely recalling these two instances.

In considerations dealing with the author of the Book of Ezekiel we have so far exclusively used arguments resulting from the engineering investigation of the text. In this matter it is further necessary, however, to listen to what those commentators have to say who have approached the problem from a religious and a linguistic angle. In the short summary which follows we present quotations containing important statements by the two commentators consulted so far. Reference 4 contains the following remarks:

> *A closer study reveals . . . the hand of a redactor. The text is sometimes in considerable disorder . . . There are also many repetitions.*
>
> *. . . [Bertholet] assumes that the prophet only left detached leaves and sketches of prophecies expanded into the present book by the spiritual heirs.* (p. 604, letter c)

After a comparative study of the ancient texts the conclusion reads:

> *We may now ascribe more probably and naturally the whole book to a single translator.* (p. 604, letter c)

Thus Ezekiel is ruled out as the direct author of the traditional book.

The view upheld in Reference 6 sounds at first somewhat surprising:

> *There had never been doubt cast upon the unity of the book . . . some scholars . . . advanced the theory that "considerable additions have been made to this work. . . ." The difficulties found in the text to support this theory are groundless and artificial. The methodical composition of the book from beginning to end is evidence that it is*

the work of one man. The conservative scholar, Kirk-
patrick, confirms the traditional view: "The Book of
Ezekiel bears the marks of careful plan and arrangement,
and comes to us in all probability direct from the prophet
himself. He speaks throughout in the first person." (p. 14)

However, immediately afterward, as the commentary
continues, we read:

While Ezekiel is the author of the book in its entirety,
the final copy for inclusion in the canon was not written
by him . . . [it was] authoritatively revised and issued
by the men of the Great Synagogue.

So here again we find an opinion that we are not in
possession of Ezekiel's original writing, but have a revised text before us.

Having thus analyzed the statements in the Book of
Ezekiel with reference to their technical contents and
deduced certain conclusions it is now appropriate to
consider its essential relationships in the light of the
knowledge acquired. We proved that Ezekiel indeed encountered spaceships, that he describes them with astonishing accuracy and that he also reports events related to
them. In the course of these investigations it was tacitly
assumed that the nontechnical parts of Ezekiel's report
are visions.

In the Biblical report the spaceship always appears as
an introduction to and twice also as a conclusion of
episodes. In the course of such episodes someone whom
Ezekiel calls "man" or "he" gives Ezekiel instructions
or describes events to him. Sometimes Ezekiel speaks
too, so that conversations occur, which however are
always very short. It is clear that the spoken parts are
the essential ones from the religious point of view: they
represent the spiritual nucleus. Even if the spaceships
are considered—in the spirit of the religious commentators—as divine throne-carrying chariots they would still
be regarded as accessories, as a means of carrying a
message but not as an essential part thereof. In a religious sense, the significance of the vehicle is definitely
less than that of the message.

Motivated as we were by a technical interest, we have so far concentrated our investigation on the vehicle, and we have proved that it was a very real spaceship. But this realization confronts us with a conflict resulting from the incompatibility of visions and physical presence of spaceships. This conflict can be resolved in two very different ways!

We arrive at the first solution by initially complicating the situation by recognizing both elements—spaceships and visions—as actual events. We do so by saying: Ezekiel both saw the spaceships and the various activities related to them and had genuine visions. The step toward the solution consists then of the assumption of a separation in time of these two elements. Such a separation in turn implies that visions took place at a point in time different from that of the encounters with spaceships. In such a case it is not relevant whether the visions were separated from the encounter by weeks or by years. Even the Biblical texts suggest this, because a period of some nineteen years separates the third from the fourth encounters and most of the visions pertain to this period.

We have already discussed the combination of vision and physical encounter. Such an amalgamation was probably caused by unawareness of the true nature of events; it is the only link between spaceship and vision! With the above clarification of its background we have done away with this link and can therefore accept the separation in time as a credible solution.

The second solution is fundamentally different. As we often did in the past, we again accept the literal meaning of what Ezekiel says. Having made this decision we are compelled to consider the encounters with the spaceships and the pertinent injunctions and descriptions as simultaneous, that is, pertaining to the same event. However, since we have proved the spaceships and commanders to have been tangible realities, the spoken parts perforce become statements made by the commander and thus lose their character of visions. Of course this in no way affects the conclusion drawn earlier with regard to the authorship of the report which has come down to us.

This alternative solution is, on one hand, the result of the logical conclusion just outlined; on the other hand, despite its unusual character, it derives more support from the existing literature than one might expect.

First of all, we find that Ezekiel's book was the center of controversies which have lasted over centuries. The keynote to all problems seems to be best expressed in Reference 6, where we read:

> Had it not been for him, the Book of Ezekiel would have been withdrawn, because its words seem to contradict the teachings of the Torah. (p. xiii)

The man to whom the salvaging of the Book is thus attributed is Rabbi Chananiah. He lived in the first century A.D. and he studied the report in depth and over a long time. It must have been a really long time because he consumed three hundred barrels of oil for light and food over that period. His written commentary in which "he reconciled all discrepancies" (Reference 6, page xiv) has apparently not been preserved but it has the priceless merit of having saved Ezekiel's book for the benefit of all of us. Nonetheless, Reference 6 concludes as follows:

> Yet, despite this Rabbi's efforts at harmonization, many divergencies were detected between the Book and the Mosaic code which baffled all attempts at reconciliation. (p. xiv)

We are thus informed of the existence of injunctions in the visionary part which differ in a way which cannot be reconciled with the Mosaic Law, that is, with fundamental principles. When we consider more specific problems we find in Reference 6 also the following remarkable comments:

> Ezekiel is unique among the Hebrew prophets both in the nature of his vision and in his mode of expression. He is the only prophet who was addressed by the title "son of man," the phrase occurring about a hundred times in the book. (p. ix)
> The style and diction of Ezekiel are also different from those of others prophets. (p. x)

We read further on the same page:

> *The allegation of some critics that Ezekiel was unable to distinguish between the ritual and moral elements in religion, since he coupled high social morality with ritualistic demands . . . Ezekiel has even been accused of caring for nothing but the externals of religion.* (p. x)

And finally again:

> *The text of the concluding chapters, dealing with the Temple of the future, presents almost insurmountable difficulties. The types and number of sacrifices prescribed there differ from those mentioned in the Pentateuch, and there are many innovations which, according to the accepted law, are normally beyond the authority of a prophet to institute.* (p. xi)

Similarly, we learn the following from Reference 4:

> *He ignores important legal institutions of earlier date and adopts those which suit his purpose . . . He insists on a sincere conversation with Yahweh, on a new heart and spirit.* (p. 603, para. 478d)
>
> *That is why his Messianism is so distinctly national and material and why a literal fulfillment of many of his prophecies cannot be expected . . .* (p. 603, para. 479a)
>
> *Torrey, 1930, regards the whole book as a pseudoepigraph, composed circa 230 B.C., fictionally ascribed to the time of Manasses by its original author and transformed into a post-exilic work by a redactor.* (p. 604, para. 479d)

To continue with our trend of thought we shall now revert to the report. One of the special features of the third encounter is the seven men summoned by the commander after the landing. Six of them are dressed in the fashion of the land, they are all referred to as those "in charge of the city" and it is therefore legitimate to assume that they had been staying in that region for a long time. If so, it may be inferred that they were familiar with customs, patterns of conduct, and religious ritual. Beyond this, arguments expounded in the next part of this book with regard to the mission of these visitors point to their very probable extensive familiarity with the cultural and political situation prevailing in a large geographical area. Among the religions encountered they must certainly have recognized the significance and value of the Jewish faith. A knowledge so acquired does not mean, of course, true understanding and assimilation. Injunctions handed down from such a "theoretical" position must, quite naturally, include mistakes. Specific aspects and motivations are either not known or incorrectly appreciated. All this is not surprising. It would be much more surprising if the commentators were *unable* to find grounds for the comments quoted above. These comments cover literally all the mistakes that could be made by somebody finding himself in the situation of those visitors: overstressing external, national, and material aspects, incorrect descriptions of sacrifices, overlooking existing laws, ignorance and therefore transgression of limits within which changes could be demanded.

To conclude the discussion of this second solution, let us bring in yet another word spoken during the first encounter as the commander begins to give his instructions to Ezekiel. He says:

3:5. For you are not sent to a people of foreign speech and a hard language, but to the house of Israel.

3:6. Not to many peoples of foreign speech and a hard language whose words you cannot understand. . . .

The striking feature of this passage is the purely personal note which is sounded in it from a double point of view. The commander obviously tries to calm Ezekiel. He talks to him "man to man" as it were, and explains to him with much emphasis that he is not expected to go to a people or peoples "of foreign speech and a hard language whose words you cannot understand." In addition we get the impression that somebody is speaking who is aware of this difficulty from his own experience, one who knows what is involved in learning vocabulary, grammar, and the correct pronunciation of a foreign language.

And how could this not be present in the memory of the commander, who has had to learn Hebrew himself?

In the following section of this book we will review the possible reasons which might have prompted the commander to talk with Ezekiel. For the time being we see, however, that this second solution, which is the logical sequel of the proof of actual encounters with spaceships, has remarkable points in its favor. To establish whether it is indeed valid goes beyond my competence and also beyond the objectives of the present investigation.

8

THE MISSION

THE question of what was the purpose, the task of those visits, is both natural and legitimate. To attempt an answer, we are using the information developed thus far which contains indications that can be helpful in shedding some light on the background of the encounters, treated here under the general designation of the "mission."

It lies in the nature of things that in so doing we are leaving the realm of the provable. We merely want to afford a glimpse of what emerges as a possibility out of the knowledge acquired, and at the same time delineate a broad outline along which correction, denial, or confirmation are required.

Since we—meaning mankind—are today relatively close to a comparable situation, there exists, on the one hand, a certain danger of the answer being influenced by our own opinions; on the other hand, however, increased familiarity with relevant problems makes an improved understanding possible. To eliminate subjective influences as much as possible we will first define the points of reference directly connected with and arising out of the investigation carried out so far. Following that, we will discuss such points as may either be deduced therefrom or inferred from the knowledge we have today. We can describe the two latter groups as indirect points of reference. The joint scrutiny of all these indications will then enable us to draw certain conclusions.

Of the four direct points of reference the one most easily perceived is the clearly peaceful manner of making contacts with humans. Nowhere can even the slightest sign of any hostility or reckless attitude be detected. On the contrary, at the outset of the two first encounters —which means during the very first contacts—we see how much care the commander shows for Ezekiel. During the fourth encounter the peaceful intent is clearly emphasized by the fact that the purpose of the tour is informative and educational. We learn this from the very words of Ezekiel's companion on that tour:

> **40:4.** And the man said to me: "Son of man, look with your eyes and hear with your ears, and set your mind upon all that I shall show you, for you were brought here in order that I might show it to you; declare all that you see to the house of Israel."

Neither compulsion nor violence are felt in this speech, but only an urgent admonition and the setting of a task.

The order to kill and its execution during the third encounter have already been discussed at length; there is no doubt at all that this episode in its present form lies outside the course of actual events and should therefore not be taken into account in an evaluation of the attitude of the visitors.

The next direct point of reference can be best expressed by the use of the word "precaution." This precaution is reflected in multiple ways in the basic layout of the spacecraft. We find it, for example, in the use and the arrangement of the helicopters. They not only make unlimited terrestrial flights possible but are also used in the landing after the descent from orbit. This enables the commander to choose landing sites at will, including sites far removed from the point at which the flight from the mothership to the earth is directly aimed.

Moreover the fire danger incident upon a landing by rocket engine on land areas covered by grass or bushes is entirely eliminated through the use of helicopters. Here we are touching again upon the already discussed theme of peaceful intentions. A landing made with the aid of a rocket engine—which was of course possible —could cause damage to vegetation and possibly to livestock in settled areas. Even people could be injured or killed. A spacecraft which is about to fly from the earth back into orbit may—as can well be expected—be surrounded by onlookers who could be seriously injured should rocket engines be used. Just a few such incidents would suffice to turn the initial wonder of the people into hostility. Such a reaction is most undesirable in a peaceful undertaking the program of which includes contacts with humans, and must therefore be avoided. The use of helicopters is an excellent solution to this problem.

Two other technical features fall within this concept of precaution. They are, on the one hand, the wheels— of which the best justification so far was related to a precise positioning of the spaceship for telecommunication purposes. On the other hand the arrangement allowed the helicopters to be jettisoned. The radical reduction in the weight of the spacecraft thus made possible could be decisive in an emergency.

A further direct point of reference is supplied by the presence of a ground crew during the third encounter. It gives us an indication of an action going beyond simple encounters with Ezekiel. The latter, consequently, loses his central position in the mission (without thereby losing it for us) and we get the impression of an undertaking planned on a larger scale.

Finally the men and their relationship to the commander as well as the presence of a guide during the fourth encounter give us a clear indication pointing to an organization. Such a conclusion could already be drawn from the assumption—which has just been substantiated—of planning on a larger scale. But in addition to this we find a definite relationship of subordination between the ground crew and the commander as well as a suggestion of a difference in rank between commander and guide. Differences of rank can thus be detected and such differences are a characteristic of any organization.

All indirect indications hinge on the already briefly mentioned economic feasibility of an undertaking. We know from our own experience of the infancy of space travel that the financial resources required are very considerable even for the big powers taking part in this activity. If we want to avoid digressing into the science fiction area, we must assume also that even the highest developed civilizations have to engage in financial planning of their constructions and projects. The idea underlying the total expenditure defines the mission which can itself be traced back to the simple question: "Why do we want to go there and what do we want to do there?" Even in the face of the basic obligation incumbent on a society capable of such feats, this question must be asked and answered. I do not mean this in a political but in a technical and economic sense because the answer determines the tasks, the design, and the financial planning.

Before we return from these general considerations to our main topic we should draw attention to a feature common to all travels, be it a weekend excursion or a spaceflight: at a given level of costs of travel and subsistence the expenses at the end point of a trip have but little impact on the total amount spent. For example, whether an astronaut covers a distance of five or fifty miles on the moon will make a negligible difference in the overall cost of the roundtrip earth-moon-earth. The considerable broadening and deepening of knowledge is out of proportion to the very small increase in the expense. In this we stress the word "knowledge" because, to stay with the same example, it would be absurd to calculate the cost per pound of rocks gathered. These moon rocks have a significance only because of the knowledge and the information they convey to us. And the knowledge is what counts, not the quantity of stones. So far as an extension of activities is at all possible at the end point of a trip, its achievement—in addition to the intellectual and idealistic obligation which exists anyway—becomes imperative even from an economic point of view.

If we now apply these considerations to Ezekiel's encounters, we arrive in the first place at the unavoidable conclusion that he could in no case have been the only target of these visitors. On grounds to be discussed later we shall realize that he was not even their most important target. Ezekiel himself supports this view very pointedly at the end of the third encounter by the description of the departure of the very same spacecraft on which he came. It departs without him and it is obvious that it has other tasks to perform. Ezekiel is taken home by another spacecraft which was summoned only because of the critical manipulation carried out on the first one. The commander of that second spaceship had therefore been at work somewhere else and his tasks were thus basically independent of Ezekiel.

Apart from these various indications and references we read that the commander speaks to Ezekiel, takes him on flights, and shows him buildings. How then can we connect all these individual observations with each other and what kind of a picture would emerge as a result?

We begin with the proven peacefulness of the visitors and combine that fact with the well-substantiated concept of an undertaking that goes beyond the short contacts with Ezekiel and that is therefore not exclusively connected with him. In other words, we see a peaceful project which encompasses an area as yet undefined in terms of geography and time. Since we do not know of any influence of such an undertaking on the history of mankind—a topic to which we shall revert later—we come to the natural conclusion that we are dealing with a reconnaissance mission. All the information we can derive from Ezekiel's report points with certainty to the fact that these visitors already knew the earth and its inhabitants quite well. It would be futile to try to deduce from Ezekiel's information how long they had already been here. Sheer probability would suggest that the encounters took place neither at the beginning nor at the end of their mission but rather "at some time" in the course of the project.

The elimination of a narrow limitation of the visits in terms of time and geography leads to the assumption of a larger program, probably including repeated visits to the earth. The events described by Ezekiel are thus mere episodes. It is of course impossible to infer from the material developed here what the tasks and the purpose of the program may have been. However, in this regard, we can have some idea of them on the basis of our own situation and knowledge. For example, as an initial incentive, we can assume general interest in the earth as a planet and beyond that as a planet which may be inhabitable. In such a case an exploration of geography and life-forms would have priority.

However, as the first visit may have already revealed that the planet Earth was inhabited, an immediate expansion of the exploration would necessarily follow, which would entail including the study of human beings in the program. Whether that initial step was followed by the encounters discussed here a few years or many thousands of years later cannot be ascertained.

With regard to all these explorations, the geographical location of the region in which Ezekiel lived is most significant. It is situated on the relatively narrow strip of land linking the two huge land masses of Eurasia and Africa. This location, clearly marked by the Mediterranean, the Red Sea, and the Persian Gulf, is most conspicuous and therefore easy to find and to describe. Thus, it is ideally suited both for arrival from space and as a starting point for the direct exploration of the earth. Finally, it possesses yet another feature that may not be a deciding factor in selecting the location of a base of operations, but that, nevertheless, is a welcome addition in the sense that it can facilitate a closer study of the earth and its inhabitants: Europe, Asia, and Africa can easily be reached by air from this point without flights over expanses of water. The flying distance to the coastline of China is roughly the same as that to South Africa. This region is therefore almost exactly in the middle between the most remote points of the area to be

explored. The distance to the farthest limits of Europe
is shorter. Thus many arguments are in favor of the
preferential role of the strip of land between the Mediterranean and the Persian Gulf. On the whole of our planet
there is only one other point possessing equally outstanding features in that regard: the Central American
land bridge between North and South America.

The general exploration of our earth and its carto-
grapic survey is however of little interest in the context
of the questions we are studying. Nonetheless, to show
that they are compatible with the other objectives of the
mission, a brief discussion of the technical aspects of
possible flights is in order. The simplest method for a
global observation is a polar orbit, that is an orbit over
both the north and the south poles. Let us imagine this
orbit as a circle crossing or almost crossing the imaginary axis of the earth over the two poles at a certain
distance from the earth's surface. Since the earth is turning beneath this circle, the passengers of the spaceship
can observe all the regions of the earth and survey and
document them according to the means available to
them. In addition, this orbit means that one is able to
land at any point of the globe, independently of its geographical longtitude and latitude. As it follows its polar
orbit, the vehicle moves from south to north on one side
of the earth and, as it continues its circling, it flies from
north to south on the other side. The trajectory of a
spacecraft flying from the mothership to the earth follows the same directions and, in this connection, we
recall Ezekiel's statement at the outset of the first encounter:

1:4. As I looked, behold, a stormy wind came out of
the north, and a great cloud, with brightness round
about it, and fire flashing forth continually . . .

The polar orbit is particularly favorable for surveys
and observation of the earth and it also makes landing
possible at any point of the globe. Yet it has a disadvantage with regard to return flights from the earth to
the mothership. This disadvantage may best be illustrated by considering, as an example, a lift-off from the

equator or a low latitude. A point located on the equator moves at a speed of roughly 1040 miles per hour around the axis of the earth. This speed decreases first gradually and then faster with increasing latitude, yet it still accounts for a noteworthy portion of the velocity needed by the spacecraft to reach orbit. Now, when the orbit goes over the poles, this initial velocity is of course not effective and must be compensated for by a longer burning time of the engine, which means higher propellant consumption. For missions aimed mainly at a landing on earth, the most favorable orbit of the mothership is one whose inclination to the equator can be adjusted to the latitude of the terrestrial location of lift-off. In that case, too, observations of regions farther to the south or to the north would of course be possible through manned or unmanned special flights.

The technical feasibility and compatibility of all these possibilities with the various tasks of the spacecraft is therefore beyond question. It cannot of course be ascertained what options were actually chosen. Nor can we ascertain the ratio of explorations of geography and living conditions compared to explorations with humans as their object. This applies both to the amount of time and the resources invested in the effort.

Also, no clues exist to help us in the assessment of the total extent of the operation that led to the encounters with Ezekiel. However, we do have some information on its lowest limits, that is, the minimum effort known to us.

With respect to the time involved we know that a twenty-year period elapsed between Ezekiel's first and last encounters.

The resources available to the operation must have consisted of at least two spaceships, if we assume that in all four encounters Ezekiel always saw the same spaceship and that only one additional vehicle was present during the third encounter. Should this assumption be wrong, he saw five spaceships at most. In any case all spacecraft were clearly of the same type. In the area of equipment four different types are mentioned: those of the six men and the "writer's tool" during the third encounter, the long measuring reed and the line of flax which were carried by the man during the fourth encounter. In the area of apparel, there is mention of the bright metallic suits worn by the commander and the guide (fourth encounter) and also of the protective suit of one man during the third encounter.

Finally, personnel deployment consists of the commander of the spaceship—and we do not really know whether he was the same commander on every occasion; the ground crew of six and the man in the protective suit; the unknown individual who took Ezekiel to the spaceship which had flown to the east gate at the end of the third encounter (probably the commander of the other spaceship); and finally the guide who led him through the temple complex during the fourth encounter. If we assume that the commander in all four encounters was the same, then we have a total of ten different "men."

This total assignment of resources is well explained and justified by the encounters. It is commensurate and in no way out of proportion. The most conspicuous element of that listing is the various "men" appearing as ground crew and commander. We will now study them in more detail.

The seven men of the ground crew—consistent with their description—were assigned a local task, and were therefore stationed at that place. The nature of such a task becomes clearer if we consider these men as part of an overall organization. As we surmise that this organization was intended for exploratory purposes, that local group assumes the character of an observation post, with the task of collecting and forwarding information. The information accessible to them ranges from weather to religion; but it would be futile to conjecture what they were actually seeking. Another possible task will be discussed later in this book.

Groups of such observers could be expected to be stationed at various important places, unless one accepts the idea that through some kind of rare coincidence Ezekiel just happened to see the only one in existence.

The commander's task is distinctly different from that of the ground crew. That crew was posted at a certain place to perform a task which we have classified as one of exploration and data collection. The commander, on the other hand, had mobility and was not bound to any given site. As we know from the third encounter he was of a higher rank than the ground crew. In his contacts with Ezekiel he is never the one who seeks information but very clearly the one who has something to give, to impart. This last point shows the essential difference between him and the ground crew.

The difference of apparel may be the expression of this fundamental difference in the nature of the respective tasks. As we saw, the commander wore a suit which protected him against excessive heat; the ground crew, on the other hand, was clad in the fashion of ordinary people of that time. Accordingly, the climate of that region was too hot for the commander, while it was bearable for the seven men. Since we suppose that both commander and crew came from the same original climate, the above statement seems to contain a contradiction.

We commence the elimination of this contradiction with the commander. He protects himself against the heat and therefore apparently comes from a climate with temperatures considerably lower than those of the region we are discussing. The crew, as we already stated, must have had the same place of origin. Let us then assume, as an example, that they all originated from a climate comparable to that of northern Scandinavia, Alaska, or Siberia, and let us apply the following example to our own physical capabilities. A person coming from such regions to the desert can become adjusted to the environment if he stays there long enough. His body will adapt itself by food, way of life, and if necessary medications. But a brief exposure does not allow the body time for such adjustment and means a heavy burden for it especially if accompanied by strenuous activity. A light and comfortable suit providing the body with a controlled environment is a great help and relief in such a case.

Accordingly, unlike the crew, the commander stays

on the ground only for a short time and we can detect therein a facet of the organizational scheme involved: crews are stationed at various sites, their task consists of gathering data and transmitting it to the mothership. From that ship, which stays aloft, envoys of higher rank (whom we have called commanders because of their connection with the spaceships) come down to fulfill special assignments of short duration.

As Ezekiel's experiences show, one of these assignments was to establish contact with men. In such cases—at least on the basis of what we could learn to date—man was not the source but the recipient of information. This fact is documented beyond any possible doubt at the beginning of the fourth encounter as reflected in the spoken admonition to pay attention. Alone this one passage would justify the conclusion that Ezekiel learned more than we would think at first. Furthermore, in section 7 of this book we have discussed the possibility that the nontechnical parts of Ezekiel's book can be regarded as messages from the commander. Should this be correct, we would have ample material regarding conveyance of information to Ezekiel. But even without this contribution there are enough signs that this could have taken place.

Summing up, we can therefore define the following three groups as the objectives of the program: exploration of the planet, observation and study of man, and intellectual influence on mankind.

As a follow up to this thought, we find yet another area where the tasks of the ground crew could be expanded and we shall put it in the form of a question: Could they not—stationed as they were at important points—also participate in the function of teaching and influencing? They doubtless had suitable opportunities to do so.

We have now, as far as this was possible, explored the objectives and the organization of the project. The question remains: Why was it Ezekiel who was repeatedly contacted?

The two obvious versions of a possible answer are planning and coincidence. A planned contact becomes plausible when we recall the existence of the ground crew. The community of Jewish exiles in Tel-Abib could, for a variety of reasons, have been of much interest to the observers. Within that community, already as a priest, Ezekiel must have been of particular importance to them. His superior intelligence must have drawn attention and further enhanced his importance. No wonder then that they proposed him to their superiors for special tasks.

On the other hand, if we speak of an accidental meeting, we certainly do not mean one single landing of the commander which, by sheer chance, brought him and Ezekiel together. Many such landings have most probably taken place. It seems, however, that the space travelers' problem was that the "normal" human being they contacted used to run away (compare Daniel, Chapter 10, Verse 7). In one of these landings, however, the commander met with a rare exception: A "son of man" * did not run away! He threw himself on the ground as a sign of submission and was obviously excited—but he stayed! He looked intelligent, gave apposite answers, and it took little experience for the commander to realize almost immediately the importance of this encounter.

Both answers, planning as well as chance, thus lead to the same point: the commander finds in Ezekiel a son of man who can be utilized exceptionally well. He knows that he will have to take him on flights later; but he also knows—either through deep understanding and empathy or from earlier experiences and reports—that these men can have strong reactions to the experience of flying which is alien to them. It therefore seems best to test out immediately this son of man who makes such

---

* With regard to this expression we must first refer to Reference 6, p. 9, where it is expressly stated that it has no relation whatsoever with a messianic significance. Reference 4, p. 605, letter h, equates this expression with the word "man." It is quite natural for the commander—in speaking to a human being—to use as a form of address the very name that that being calls itself by. In the absence of a better comparison it can be pointed out that we, too, often use names of species, as for instance when we talk to animals.

a promising impression, by taking him up on a short flight.

The question posed above: Why Ezekiel, the man? can also be put in the following words: Why Ezekiel, the Jew? We derive the answer from the two first-mentioned objectives of the visit. We can infer therefrom that those visitors were familiar with the cultures and religions of a large part of the earth. Therefore they must doubtless have recognized the high potential of the Jewish creed, its superiority over the other contemporary religions; they were equally aware of the political and religious difficulties of the Jews at that time. It is therefore conceivable that they may have wished to bring consolation and reassurance to the Jews, and of course especially to those who live in exile. On this point, incidentally, the interpretation given here agrees with the traditional version. From the viewpoint of a very advanced civilization the wish to counteract an acute threat such as the one inherent in the situation of the Jews at that time would be quite understandable.*

To be able to see the behavior of these visitors in the proper light, we must remember that their mission was a peaceful one, that it included a mandate to explore and was definitely not undertaken in order to prepare an invasion. The history of mankind has, in the meantime, convincingly proved this. These visitors, therefore, knew that their stay on earth was limited in time. This circumstance shows how much their ethical and also their political level was different from our own today. To make this clearer, let us exchange the roles and attribute our own mentality of the twentieth century to the commander and the ground crew. Would *we* be able to muster so much trust in the intelligence of others and so much faith in the fertility of ideas to try to strengthen *only* the faith of these beings in their people and their religion? Would we really prefer natural growth to as-

---

* We saw in this activity of the commander *one* of his tasks (p. 134). It would be interesting in future studies to look for indications of further tasks and to establish whether intellectual influence can be inferred also from other reports.

sistance by superior material power which could only be effective for a short time? In this regard we are further removed from them than by the few decades which seem to separate us in terms of technological and scientific achievement.

Many questions remain unanswered. Will we ever be able to establish when these visits to the earth began? Or will we at least be able to prove conclusively that there have been earlier and later visits?

When did they end? And did they?

9

FORM AND MECHANISM

EZEKIEL describes the commander (or commanders), the ground crew of the third encounter, and his guide during the fourth encounter always and only with the short words "man" or "men" or "likeness of a man." On no occasion does he say more. The same observer, who possesses such an outstanding perception, finds nothing worthy of mention about them other than the fact of their presence. His treatment of their clothes is analogous; he does not mention them as long as there is nothing special about them; but he always does whenever they are different from the ordinary, the expected.

Curiously enough this very absence of description conveys to us quite an accurate picture of these "men"; it shows, namely, that these visitors really looked like ordinary men, and that their appearance was within the range of such variations as might normally have been expected in Ezekiel's times with respect to size, weight, and color of skin. An additional indication may be inferred from Ezekiel's flights in the spaceship. Since he fitted into the seat in the command capsule, these beings were certainly not substantially smaller or thinner than he was.

From everything we could learn we must therefore conclude that in their appearance these visitors possessed characteristics of the human form, that the maximum deviations in their height could not have exceeded some

eight inches, more or less, from the average height of
the people of those days, and that their proportions (such
as, for example, the waistline) were also fairly consistent
with the average values of their human contemporaries.

We know, however, that biochemistry has made us
aware of forms of "life" very different from those we
are familiar with. To expound such knowledge into the
area of highly developed organisms would necessarily
include the idea that their appearance may be entirely
different from ours. These doubtlessly justified considerations have, however, had the effect of focusing the
thinking on this particular possibility—of an appearance
other than ours—thus obscuring the possibility of a resemblance to the outward appearance of man. This is
why I feel that this latter possibility merits closer investigation. To accomplish this I shall explore the question of form from the point of view of the mechanical
system involved (or from the point of view of a design
engineer, which is the same) and briefly define the
underlying fundamentals. The legitimacy of such considerations is evident: the overall system which we can
describe as the "intelligent being" must not only be
chemically, biologically, and mentally self-sustaining
and capable of development, but its structure must be
such as to ensure the equally important mechanical functions. The invariable basic requirements of the latter are
the ability to move and the operation of tools (needed
for the intake of food, for the ability to fight, and to
shape materials).

No matter how high the level of development of a
civilization, it needs the full industrial spectrum ranging
from mining and heavy industry to high-precision processes which may not even be known to us. And even if
—for unfathomable reasons—it should no longer require
all this, it must have had it at the stage of its development comparable to our own today.* The individual
beings making up this society must be able to cope with

---

* Since we are talking about evolution, we automatically rule
out the spontaneous creation of a ready-made highly advanced
civilization.

such conditions which again means that they must be able to fulfill functions similar to those of humans.

To be able to study the influence of mechanical requirements on the form, we must consider and treat the latter as a mechanical system. That system must be capable of the following functions:

> Observation, evaluation, command (combined in a control center)
> Change of place (movement)
> Operations
> Conversion of energy

The first and the last of the functions listed above are, it is true, of a nonmechanical nature, yet an advantageous location within the overall system of the structures they require is beyond question a matter of design.

There are sufficient reasons to eliminate flying and swimming beings from this investigation, so that it only remains for us to consider a being which moves on solid ground and is surrounded by a gaseous mixture. The guideline for the basic layout of our "structure" may be established as follows: For understandable reasons the "control center" must be arranged as high as possible above the ground. The parts required for the conversion of energy must therefore necessarily be arranged between the control center and the organs of motion which are in contact with the ground. The location of operational organs (tools) does not lend itself to such a direct definition. Yet it may be inferred from the need for multiple utilization of the mechanism that they should be located as far as possible from the organs of locomotion.

With the aid of certain mechanical concepts we can proceed from this general scheme of distribution to the identification of corresponding forms. With the exception of "force," the most essential concept in mechanics is the "moment," which is the product of force and a distance. We owe to the moment the important element in mechanics—the lever. We must acknowledge that these fundamentals have universal validity; just as we do for the inclined plane, friction, and the wheel.

Movements of the system result as a consequence of moments. Since, for structural reasons, the wheel is eliminated as a design element of nature, the use of the lever remains the only way to produce movement, and it necessarily entails structures similar to the leg, the arm, and the hand. The optimum number of legs, arms, and fingers may be a matter of argument and the same applies to the optimum number of joints in all these limbs. In addition, we know the minimum requirements: two legs, two arms, and hands with three fingers each. There are good reasons for concluding that in the case of legs and arms the optimum coincides with the minimum, which therefore explains the existence of these limbs in pairs. But such is not the case for the hands, of which it can only be said that they should probably be equipped with at least four but probably not more than six fingers each (for example, two thumbs, one at each end of the row of fingers). In any case, one can expect more than three fingers to a hand.

As we see, this investigation—which, as we said before, is here merely outlined in its basic essentials—leads to a structure which has all the basic characteristics of a human body. We have recognized that the entity "form = mechanical system" uses particularly one of the basic elements of mechanics, the lever. The mechanical consistency in the structure and the universal validity of the lever and of the law which governs it make this entity operative regardless of its location in the universe and show us that the design of the human body is neither unique, earthbound, nor coincidental, but that it possesses general validity.

I would like to offer a strictly technical example in support of this statement. It concerns the mechanical arms and hands developed over many years for tasks ranging from the servicing of "hot" reactors to underwater operations. The more refined such designs are, the closer their appearance approaches the shapes of human hands and arms (compare Figs. 8a and 8b). This result is significant because it is certainly not due to preconceived planning. It is in fact the result of the work of groups, which independently were searching objectively for the most appropriate principles and designs.*

This much for the outward shape. The desirable insight into the basic characteristics of the internal structure of the mechanical system will be obtained by the following additional considerations.

The mention of a highly advanced extraterrestrial civilization immediately makes us think of its technology which enables it to make contact with us. But it is self-evident that such a civilization must also have yet another form of expression: its art. A brief discussion of the dependence of art on mechanisms is needed to enable us to proceed with our investigation. We are, of course, not talking about an "essential," but a purely mechanical dependence. We will explain this by an example taken from our own art forms: a string quartet, a Persian miniature, a Chinese jade sculpture would be inconceivable if our hands were shaped like those of a frog, or the paws of a dog, or the hands of an anthropoid ape. Even the writing of a poem or a musical score requires the mechanism we call a hand. From these few remarks two important requirements emerge as prerequisites for any activity in the sphere of arts: articulation and sensitivity.

The self-evident presence of art-related activities within the framework of a highly advanced civilization demands the existence of the same properties in its members. Sensitivity is particularly relevant to our argument because it means that the surface of such beings cannot consist of a shell or calluslike wrapping but must be made of a substance which, broadly speaking, is en-

---

* For a demonstration of an example in reverse I invite the participation of the reader. Please place your forearm on the table by which you are sitting so that your hand lies in front of your chest. Now raise the hand and the forearm and grasp an object which is a short distance from your hand. Observe purely optically, that is, without thinking of what you feel in your hand or arm, how hand, arm, and fingers move exactly as an industrial gripping device does. The close relationship between nature and technology is unmistakable.

dowed with the properties of human skin. Proceeding from this premise, we can conclude with a high degree of probability that they must also have a skeleton as a "supporting structure."

Summing up, we can therefore say that—particularly because of the universal validity of the law of the lever —the general appearance of the human form can likewise, and with very high probability, be assumed to be universal. The likely existence of skeleton and skin is deduced from the necessary presence of articulation and sensitivity. Such visitors may therefore be expected with a great degree of certainty to look "like a man."

10

WIDENING THE BASIS

THE engineering evidence presented in this book follows the logic of algebra which says that if $A = B$ and $B = C$, then $A = C$. In our case these symbols mean:

- A. Presentation in the original text;
- B. Identification of text with known technical forms in a general way;
- C. Analysis and reconstruction proving that the general presentation indicates—in this particular case —not only a possible but also a meaningful technical entity.

It is important to recognize that in the equation $B = C$, value B already represents a technical concept which, while it was inspired by the original text ($A = B$), nonetheless wholly consists of elements pertaining to our times. This equation is therefore entirely technical and the spacecraft expressed by the symbol C is an independent technical entity. In our case, the argument is further strengthened by descriptions of events whose course agrees perfectly with our reconstruction.

To wish to negate this self-contained evidence by continuing to speak of vision, dream, hallucination, or poetic invention means to accept a long series of coincidences which would indeed be needed to substantiate all the congruities we have proved here. A juxtaposition of this acceptance of chance with the analytical and structural argumentation illustrates best how untenable the former attitude is.

We owe everything acquired so far to Ezekiel's superior abilities. With his help a basis could be created which is reserved for future studies to broaden. The question now arises: Are there indeed other reports which, regardless of their form, speak to us of such events?

As we think of the size of the spaceships, of the noise they make, and of other attending circumstances, we have no choice but to assume that there must have been observations by other men too. The material available for further search and study in the form of ancient writings, legends, and archaeological findings is of enormous volume. It is not really probable that Ezekiel's book is the only report containing statements of such great scope. Probably there exist other reports too of comparable quality of content, even though we may not yet be aware of them. On the other hand, we may well expect to find most of the reports in a veiled or fragmentary form. This applies not only to written and oral legends but particularly to archaeological discoveries because sculptures and depictions necessarily present either a scene or a symbol. As fragments such findings would have the meaning that pot shards have to archaeologists. A single piece conveys but little information; correlative and comparative research is needed to develop the mosaic of knowledge.

Another point to be considered is that perhaps Ezekiel's mental acumen is really the only instance of such kind. Moreover, in those ancient times, the total absence of technical knowledge must have prompted men more strongly to lose what they saw in what they believed; the mighty unknown would turn into the psychologically familiar, into a deity or a demon. Accordingly, the cover under which reality lies concealed will vary from epoch to epoch, and from people to people.

These thoughts lead us to recognize the need for yet another effort to broaden the basis: increased cooperation. I have already stressed and explained the need for the participation of qualified engineers. However, both at the outset and as it develops, this work requires—as an evident prerequisite—the willing cooperation of scientists and scholars in all fields where source material is available.

All such work begins as a question, a quest—the way I introduced this book. I cannot judge whether we are already *obligated* today to raise this question; it is certain, however, that we are both entitled and able to raise it. Neither the right to formulate the question nor the right to seek an answer to it can therefore be doubted or denied. Neither he who questions nor he who contributes to finding the answer should be deterred by concern over possible damage to the reputation and professional standing he may have earned by hard work.

Because it is not negation but research, not narrow-mindedness but tolerance, not divisiveness but cooperation, that lead us to progress.

And it is not our destiny to cling to the impossible—but to find the possible.

APPENDIX

A. Technical description

THE general description of the spacecraft in section 4 of this book will be supplemented here by some strictly technical information. It may be appropriate to preface it with a brief explanation.

Objectives and characteristics of the work performed here are about equivalent to a thorough preliminary design investigation conducted by a practicing engineer. The nature of such work requires the clarification of basic relationships, but not the solution of details. It is sufficient to pursue every uncertainty only up to the point at which we have full assurance that a satisfactory solution is possible. The details of the actual solution are of no significance to the overall concept. The degree of penetration of a particular case is therefore dependent on its difficulty; it may vary from a brief statement to a more elaborate secondary investigation. Naturally, the temptation is frequently strong—and was so particularly during the investigation discussed here—to go deeper into details. In this regard, however, there is an excellent saying which is attributed to the great mathematician K. F. Gauss. I remember it was printed on the first page of the logarithm tables I used in high school; it says: "Nothing shows the lack of mathematical education more clearly than excessive accuracy in calculating," and it has always reminded me, throughout the many years that have since gone by, that there are meaningful limits to accuracy and development of detail. Such limits vary certainly from task to task—yet overstepping them is always fruitless.

1. The main body

As already mentioned, the shape of the lower part of the main body was first published and discussed in Reference 8. Wind tunnel tests were conducted at the Langley Research Center of NASA in the years following that publication. Some of the reports are listed in References 10 to 14. Fig 15 shows a Schlieren photograph taken from Reference 11.

An important parameter for the definition of the lower part is the ratio of its length to its base radius. The length, in this case, is the distance from the tip to the base (station of maximum diameter). The tests conducted at Langley covered a wide range of that ratio; the value 1.0 was selected for the configuration shown in Figs. 1 and 4. The conditions for the overall layout of the spacecraft resulting from that selection were sufficient for the present purpose.

The profile of the lower part was taken directly from Reference 11, page 17. It should be possible to change this profile if desirable for the helicopter rotors.

From a structural point of view the main body is a relatively straightforward structure. It consists of stiffened shells like those used today in aircraft and rockets. Even the heat shield on the surface of the lower part is not basically new, since such structures are now being developed for NASA's Shuttle.

An exception from these aircraft-type parts of the structure is a massive ring in the area of the maximum diameter. It carries the tensile loads of the outer skin of the lower body and is therefore loaded in compression. In addition, the ring is an essential element for the introduction and distribution of the loads occurring at the attachment points of the helicopters. And finally, it is undoubtedly included also in the system of the internal structure of the main body. That combination of several

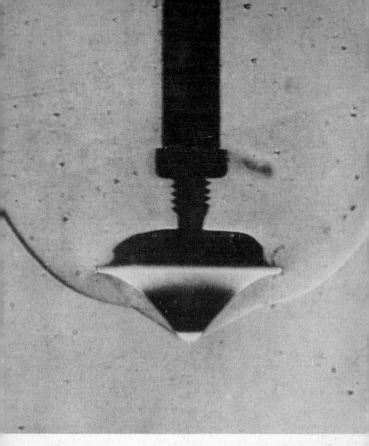

Figure 15 Lower part of main body in the wind tunnel. Schlieren photograph. Langley Research Center, NASA

purposes in one structural element results in lower structural weights and emphasizes the advantage offered by the shape of the lower body.

2. The propellant tank

The location of this tank within the main body is shown in Fig. 16. Depending on available manufacturing processes, its sides will either run parallel to the outside contour or be built up of conical rings the slope of which is adapted to the optimum curve. Space for stiffening structures, insulation, pipes, and cables must be provided between the surface and the tank.

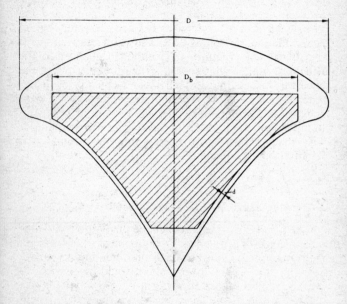

Figure 16 Cross section of main body and propellant tank

Because of the small diameter of the lower bulkhead, its location has no significant influence on the tank volume and consequently on the location of the upper bulkhead. The latter is indicated in Fig. 16 by a straight line. That does not mean that the bulkhead is actually flat, which would make it unacceptably heavy. An elliptical profile, which is almost exclusively used for bulkheads today, would likewise not be feasible for weight reasons, due to the large diameter. However, design principles have been known for years now that render bulkheads of low depth (References 15 to 17). Structures of that kind would extend beyond the indicated straight line by only a small amount. The possible introduction of structural ties between the bulkhead structure and that of the upper part of the spaceship will result in further weight savings.

The large empty volume above the tank has been reserved for the various auxiliary systems. Free space is also left between the maximum tank diameter and the vehicle surface; it was considered necessary for the accommodation of various ducts and cables as well as for the attachment structures and rotating mechanisms of the helicopter units. That space, furthermore, provides the necessary accessibility of all these elements for maintenance purposes, etc. To simplify the analysis, a constant ratio of tank diameter D_b and distance d (Fig. 16) to the maximum diameter of the vehicle was introduced. That made it possible to express the tank volume as a function of that diameter:

$$V = 0.0963D^3$$

3. The plug nozzle

The possibility of subdividing the plug nozzle into segments suggests a potential deviation from the arrangement described so far. Instead of a continuous nozzle near the "tip" of the lower part it would be possible to arrange several separated segments in the vicinity of the maximum vehicle diameter. Such an arrangement would have the advantage of a drag reduction of the upper side of the spacecraft during ascent by influencing the airflow around the rim. In a vehicle as shown in Fig. 4 this option would be uneconomical because of the great distance from the reactor and the consequently long lines it would require. In small spacecraft (see Fig. 24) that disadvantage does not exist, and such an arrangement would therefore be possible.

4. The helicopters

On page 165 we see the direct dependence of the power requirement, and the weights affected by it, on the rotor diameter. Using the configuration of Fig. 4 as a reference, we could therefore investigate potential weight reduction of the entire vehicle as a result of an increase of the rotor diameter. The latter can be achieved by changing the shape of the main body (lower height, larger diameter) or—without changing the main body—by introducing outrigger-type structures to carry the helicopters. The important aerodynamic conditions for the rotor blades would of course have to be considered in all such variations. In any case, the concave form of the lower part of the main body permits substantial variations of the arrangement of these major elements relative to each other because of its natural compatibility with the helicopter requirements. After all, it is that very geometrical compatibility which makes such a design feasible in the first place.

A brief remark, finally, concerning the column connecting helicopter and main body. It is essentially a cylindrical shell structure. Its diameter is large enough to provide a passageway for crew translation on its inside. The upper end leads into the free space inside the rim of the main body (Fig. 16 and p. 152). In combination with a suitable layout of the lower part of the helicopter body, a passageway between ground and command capsule can thus be provided.

5. The wheels

For two and one half millennia the wheel was the only structural element of the entire spaceship for which human knowledge and experience existed. It was therefore the only one that was interpreted in a technical sense—as a wheel—throughout this long period of time. Until now, all those who tried to interpret Ezekiel made the mistake of basing their findings on the *appearance* of the wheel, which is conveyed in a single short expression by the words "as though one wheel were within another" (Chapter 1, Verse 16). Since nobody knew about the reality of the spacecraft, the description of the *function* was overlooked, which is given repeatedly and clearly. It is precisely the function, however, from which the actual design can be derived and which can best serve to test the correctness of an interpretation.

In Chapter 1, Verse 17, Ezekiel says clearly: "When

they went, they went in any of their four directions without turning as they went," and again in Chapter 10, Verse 11: "When they went, they went in any of their four directions without turning as they went . . ." Another passage is of interest in this connection. It is Chapter 10, Verse 13: "As for the wheels, they were called in my hearing 'galgal' (wheel work)." All these functional descriptions indicate that the wheels could move in any direction from a given point. They also leave no doubt that these movements could be performed without any change of the orientation of the wheel relative to the spacecraft.

Before we proceed to a functionally correct interpretation of that description, it appears desirable to have a closer look at the conventional interpretation, the "crossed wheels." The concept of such a pair of intersecting wheels is a spontaneous reaction, so to speak, which has found its expression in words and pictures. For this very reason it is necessary first to show that such a solution is completely untenable. The required function states—to say it again—that the wheel can move in any direction from a given point.

Let us begin in Fig. 17 with the starting position illustrated in sketches a and b. The wheel can obviously roll in directions 1 and 2; a movement in direction 3, which is somewhat in between, is possible only if that direction lies exactly halfway between 1 and 2, that is, at an angle of 45°. In that case, however, the wheel "wobbles" considerably because it rolls on an elliptical cylinder. It has a substantially increased power consumption, makes for a most uncomfortable ride, and cannot be stopped in every position.

We now return for a moment to the starting position as shown in sketches a and b and let the wheel make a quarter turn in direction 1. It will then be in the position illustrated by sketches c and d. From here, the wheel can roll *only* in direction 1; a movement in the transverse direction would make it fall into the position shown in sketch e and thus block any further movement.

In trying yet to save the customary interpretation, one could assume the wheel to change its direction only after

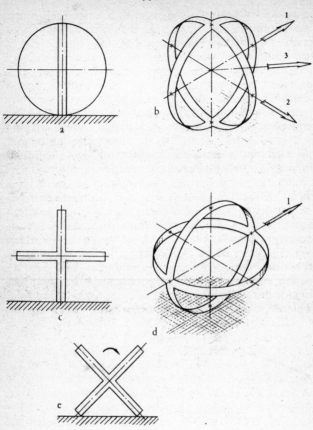

Figure 17   Characteristic positions of "crossed wheels"

half a revolution. After half a revolution its position is
exactly like the initial position and the movement could
now be continued in the direction of the second rim.
That means a course change by a right angle. The same
applies to the new direction, which means that further
course changes will again be possible only after a half
turn or multiples thereof, and each time again only by
exactly 90°. Such a course would therefore consist of

straight stretches arranged perpendicular to each other. If we consider, finally, that the wheel has a diameter of about 6½ feet, we come to realize that course changes are possible only about every 10 feet. Such a severely restricted mobility is of course entirely unacceptable, and the "crossed wheel" concept must therefore be excluded from any further consideration.

Let us now turn to the actual possibilities. The general principle allowing a functionally correct solution was discussed in section 4. The transformation of that principle into a structural design was likewise indicated there (Fig. 10). For a better understanding we will add here a description of the basic concept of the support and drive mechanism of the barrel-shaped segments. The weight of the vehicle is transferred from the spokes to these segments through supporting wheels which are arranged in pairs at the ends of the spokes as shown in Fig. 18. The surface of the supporting wheels must be spherical because of the relative motions, and they are driven individually or in pairs to achieve a rolling motion of the entire wheel perpendicular to its main plane. That drive, for which there are several known options

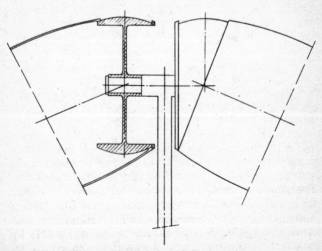

Figure 18   Support principle of the wheel segments

available, is not shown in Fig. 18. The torque is transmitted from supporting wheel to segment by a minimum of two grooves engaging two short pins which are attached to the segments.

The barrel-shaped segments can either be rigid or elastic; a wide range of choices is available for design and material selection.

A typical feature of the solution just described is the gaps interrupting the rolling surface at every spoke. It should be born in mind, however, that these wheels are used exclusively for slow movement so that such interruptions are very probably felt less than the unevenness of the ground on which the wheel rolls. It is nonetheless interesting to check whether there are feasible solutions providing a continuous rolling surface. A solution is shown in Fig. 19. Its main feature is the support of the tire R by two disks S. The outer rim surfaces of these disks have oblique grooves in which the "eyes" of the tire can slide. When both disks are driven synchronically by the gears mounted on the axle, the wheel turns in the usual direction; any difference in their speed of revolution causes the tire to rotate in the direction of arrow 2 of Fig. 9 and thus produces a controllable motion of the wheel perpendicular to its main plane. The difficulty of this solution lies in the material selection and the internal composition of the tire; it is caused by the difference between inner and outer circumferences of the tire to which an imaginary fiber must adapt during its travel along the periphery of the tire cross section. In conclusion, it should be pointed out that the wheels described here represent only basic layouts without any refinement through actual design work. Moreover, it is quite possible that additional concepts can be developed. I believe, however, that these two examples give a positive answer to the question of the feasibility of the wheel. It should be noted too that in both solutions multiple simultaneous movements can be observed on the wheel. An observer would see, apart from the familiar rolling motion, the rotation of the tire segments in one case, and in addition to the tire rotation the turning of the disks in the other. It does not seem unreasonable, therefore, to choose the description "wheel . . . within another" for

such a device, and to call it " 'galgal' (wheel work)"
(Chapter 10, Verse 13).

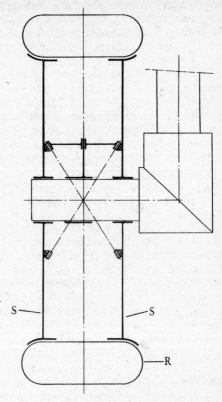

Figure 19   Design principle of a wheel with continuous tire

B. Analysis

1. System of units

The so-called Technical System of Units using meter
for length, second for time, and kilogram for weight, is
the one most widely used today. The International System of Units (*Système International d'Unités*), which
uses the physically correct unit of kilogram mass instead

of the kilogram weight, although generally accepted, is not yet in truly general use.

In order to avoid complicating the reading of this book by the use of terms familiar to only a small portion of the readers, I have used the Technical System throughout. The corresponding figures of the English system (ft. lb, etc.) are added where meaningful.

2. Procedure

The analytical investigation centers around the formula

$$\frac{W_0}{W_c} = e^{\frac{v}{g \cdot I_{sp}}}$$

which defines the conditions for a one-stage flight from earth into a desired orbit and in which

W_0 = lift-off weight, in kg (or lbs) (total weight at the beginning of the flight)

W_c = weight at the end of the flight, in kg (or lbs)

e = the natural number = 2.71828

v = velocity at the end of the flight, in m/sec (or ft/sec)

g = acceleration of gravity = 9.81 m/sec^2 (or 32.2 ft/sec^2)

I_{sp} = specific impulse, in sec

In the case of a new vehicle development the first two values are the unknowns. All other figures are either known or can be estimated. In order to eliminate one of the two unknowns, they are usually coupled by introducing the value

$$m = \frac{W_0 - W_c}{W_0}$$

In this expression, $W_0 - W_c$ represents the weight of the propellant consumed during the flight, and m indicates, therefore, the ratio of propellant weight to total weight. Since the proper definition is not in weight but in mass, m is called the mass fraction. For rockets of conventional construction or such with minor deviations, the range of the expected mass fraction is either known from experience or can be obtained by relatively simple extrapolation. The introduction of the mass fraction is therefore a very advantageous means to solve the basic equation. In the case of a subsequent development and hardware program these figures are watched closely, of course, and corrections are made when necessary.

In the present case, however, there was no way to estimate the mass fraction with an even remotely satisfactory degree of accuracy. On the other hand, it is clearly possible to obtain weight estimates of the subsystems by introducing their characteristic properties as parameters. Since it was intended from the outset to include in the investigation a wide range of the specific impulse, that value too was treated parametrically, as was, finally, also the lift-off weight over the expected range.

The easiest way to handle these many variables is a subdivision of the analysis into two parts, each of which using the lift-off weight W_0 as reference value. The first part determines the weight relations defined by the flight conditions as expressed in the formula above. In the second part, structural weights are determined as fractions of W_0. Since both parts of the analysis include the full range of the specific impulse, it is possible to superimpose their results directly. This procedure is done graphically. The points of intersection of respective curves so obtained evidently satisfy the conditions of both parts of the analysis, and are therefore part of the final result. The connection of these points to a new curve renders the graphic presentation of the end result. The accuracy of the procedure is sufficient, because it is higher than that of the underlying assumptions. These assumptions will now be discussed.

(a) Flight conditions

Lift-off Weight W_0: This weight will be considered over a range of 10,000–100,000 kilograms (22,000–220,000 lbs).

Specific Impulse I_{sp}: As already mentioned, this figure indicates how many kilograms (or lbs) of thrust will be produced for each kilogram (or lb) of propellant consumed per second. Besides that direct dependence on the type of propellant, this figure also is influenced by the engine design and by the environment, that is, it depends on whether it operates in the atmosphere or in a vacuum. Theoretical investigations have shown that this value can by far exceed the now achievable maximum of about 800–900 sec. For that reason, a range of 1000–10,000 sec was considered in the analysis.

Velocity v: This includes several component velocities, the most significant of which is determined by the orbital altitude. This amount results from the simple requirement that the centrifugal force due to the circular motion must equal the weight of the vehicle if that body is to stay in orbit. The additional velocities result from the following considerations: In order to achieve the circular orbit, the vehicle must pass through the atmosphere; that means it has to overcome aerodynamic drag; it also must overcome the gravitational attraction of the earth; and finally, its flight path must be changed from the ascent trajectory into the circular orbit. All these efforts require energy which can be expressed in velocity increases and which, in that form, is used in the basic formula. In our case the resultant total velocity for the expected orbital altitude of about 400 kilometers (220 nautical miles) (see p. 46) is about 9300 meters per second (30,500 ft/sec).

The first result is obtained by using these values in the basic formula; it is represented in Fig. 23 by the curves marked W_0.

(b) Structural weights

Introduction: The total weight can be subdivided as follows.

Structure	W_1	Main body
	W_2	Main engine
	W_3	Radiation shield
	W_4	Helicopter drive
	W_5	Rotor
	W_6	Landing gear
	W_7	Command capsule
Propellant	W_8	Braking and control
	W_9	Ascent flight
Landing	W_{10}	Touchdown weight

The structural weight of a given vehicle is constant; the propellant weight changes with the propellant consumption during flight. Since the total weight—the sum of these two major weight groups—determines the dimensions and therefore the weight of the structure, its magnitude must be determined for various phases of the operation.

Weight changes during the operation: We selected lift-off weight W_0 for the return flight into orbit as starting and reference point for all weight determinations. Using the above list we obtain the following expression:

$$W_0 = \sum_{i=1}^{7} W_i + W_9$$

In this expression we have intentionally neglected the small amount of propellant necessary to bring the spacecraft to its mothership after it has reached orbit. Next, we obtain the simple equation

$$W_c = \sum_{i=1}^{7} W_i$$

The propellant weight necessary for the return flight can then be found by introducing those values that were determined by the flight conditions in part (a) above:

$$W_9 = W_0 - W_c$$

As stated above, this term gives us the amount of propellant necessary for the return flight into orbit. That amount is not sufficient to size the propellant tank, however. For that purpose it is necessary to include the amount of propellant required for the braking during descent. Finally, there is also the propellant for the control rockets on board. Because of their relative insignificance, the two latter quantities are combined and estimated to amount to about 10 percent of W_9. The propellant tank will then be sized for the amount

$$W_8 + W_9 = 1.1 \, W_9$$

This simplification results in an insignificant oversizing of the propellant tank. Since the latter, in turn, determines the dimensions of the main body, that body also is influenced the same way. The respective weights will therefore be slightly higher than they would be as a result of a more accurate analysis.

So much for the weight W_0 for the return flight. The weight at touchdown after descent from orbit, and the weight that is to be lifted by the helicopters for the terrestrial flights, is higher by the amount of the control rocket propellant because very little of it has been consumed at that moment. This amount, however, cannot be determined at all, but it is very small. Given the uncertainty of estimates here, it is much simpler to use higher factors in the weight determination of the respective structures than to try to assess small weight differences. Consequently, we will equate the touchdown weight as well as the weight for the terrestrial flights to the lift-off weight, and we can say:

$$W_{10} = W_0$$

The influence of technology: Technology is changing constantly. Its changes parallel our penetration of the laws of nature and our ability to make use of them. On the one hand, therefore, all technological development means genuine progress while, on the other hand, it is dependent on time.

With the very broad spectrum of influences that make a technical product and achievement possible, the available materials and their properties are of particular significance. They determine to a great extent whether an idea can be implemented at a given point in time. Beyond that, they determine, in combination with the abilities of the engineers in design and fabrication, the weight of a structure. For that reason, there exists a time dependence of the structural weights which, in general, will decrease with progressing development. We are therefore entitled to consider the same tendency also for the weight estimates performed here.

The weight estimates are made in two steps. The first is the determination of weights as they can be achieved with our present state of the art; the second is the extrapolation into the future possibilities. The latter was again subdivided into two groups: one assuming a relatively modest amount of progress, and another accepting the possibility of a substantial improvement. That double extrapolation, which we will call Technology 1 and Technology 2 (abbreviated T_1 and T_2) will be used to gain insight into the length of time separating us from the realization of those structures. As far as possible, I have made use of existing information for the first step, although some assumptions on my part were unavoidable. As far as the extrapolations are concerned, they are, of course, never objective; just as in any other field, there is no sure and undebatable way to predict the future. The figures and ranges used were selected with great care, however, and by and large I believe them to be conservative.

Individual weights

W_1: Main Body. This figure includes the weight of the central main body, the propellant tank, and the helicopter support structure. As described earlier, it consists mostly of stiffened thin-walled shells. The outstanding exception is the compression ring located in the area of the largest diameter of the structure, which constitutes a substantial local weight concentration.

For our calculation it is necessary to express the weight of this group in terms of only one parameter— for which the maximum diameter is an obvious choice. We will therefore use a circular disk of a certain thickness for the weight determination. For a given level of development, thickness will be kept constant independent of diameter. The latter assumption neglects minor variations which are caused by a certain dependence of the structural thicknesses on the diameter.

The thickness of the disk is the sum of the average wall thicknesses in vertical direction of the various structures, and constitutes therefore something like a "substitute wall thickness," which also includes all internal structures. Considering present-day aluminum properties, this substitute thickness is estimated at 15 millimeters (0.59 inch). A course calculation indicates that the weight of the large compression ring will amount to about 20–30 percent of the total weight, and the thickness of the disk is therefore increased to 20 millimeters (0.79 inch).

The influence of a higher technology will be expressed by a reduction in thickness at the same specific gravity. The enormous progress made in the field of material sciences during recent years, and the prospects it indicates, allow the assumption of rather drastic reductions. The fact that buckling is less dependent on the ultimate strength than on the modulus of elasticity of a material is of only little consequence in a structure such as discussed here because its parts are mainly loaded in tension. The disk thickness will therefore be assumed to be 12 millimeters for T_1, and 9 millimeters for T_2.

The following weight figures will thus be obtained:

$$T_1 \qquad W_1 = 26.4D^2$$
$$T_2 \qquad W_1 = 19.8D^2$$

The diameter D of the main body depends on the propellant volume required for a certain total weight. We saw earlier that the ratio of tank volume and size of the main body can be kept constant and we found the expression

$$V = 0.0963D^3$$

We can determine the propellant volume V from the propellant weight 1.1 W_9 and the specific gravity of liquid hydrogen, 70.8 kg/m³ (4.4 lb/cu ft). By introducing these values in the above weight figures, we can express diameter and weight of the main body in dependence of W_0.

W_2: Main Power Plant. This consists of the reactor and the plug nozzle. In this case it is particularly difficult to arrive at a weight estimate because with regard to the reactor we are still at the beginning of a very promising development, and because, furthermore, there is only scant information available in the open literature on existing reactors. Fig. 20 shows the relationship between thrust and weight of the power plant for T_1 and T_2.

W_3: Radiation Shield. The expected values are shown in Fig. 21.

W_4: Helicopter Drive. The weight of power plants is usually expressed in terms of their performance. It is therefore necessary first to determine the power requirement of the four rotors. The weight to be lifted is W_0.

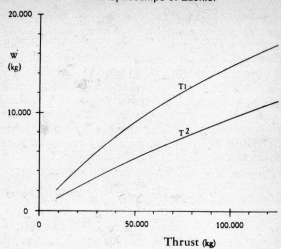

Figure 20   Weights of the main power plant

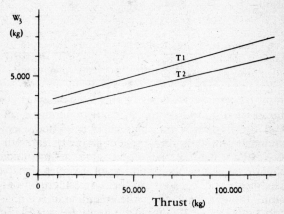

Figure 21   Weights of radiation shield

The performance required to lift that weight at a velocity v is (Reference 18):

$$N = \frac{W_0}{150\eta} \left(v + \sqrt{v^2 + 16 \cdot \frac{W_0}{A} \cdot \frac{\rho_0}{\rho}} \right)$$

For the hover flight the formula is:

$$N = \frac{W_0}{37.5\eta} \sqrt{\frac{W_0}{A} \cdot \frac{\rho_0}{\rho}}$$

where

η = airfoil efficiency

$A = \frac{\pi}{4} \cdot D_r^2$ = rotor area

ρ = air density

The use of the first formula is problematic because of uncertainty about the ascent velocity and the influence of the helicopter arrangement on aerodynamic conditions of the rotor. It is better and simpler to use the formula for the hover flight and to increase the performance figure so obtained by a certain percentage.

This is justified if we consider that we are here not calculating the dimensions of a hardware project but rather are attempting to establish approximate dimensions in order to check the feasibility of a vehicle. We will therefore assume a 20 percent performance increase and as a further precaution, a low degree of efficiency of 0.75. Under these conditions we obtain the following expression for the total power requirement of all four helicopters:

$$N = 0.024 \frac{W_0}{D_r} \sqrt{W_0}$$

This formula shows us that the power requirement decreases with increasing rotor diameter D_r. The weight calculations are made for a broader range of rotor diameters; still, it is necessary to determine the maximum possible size of the rotors. The geometrical relationships and the largest possible rotor diameter resulting therefrom are shown in Fig. 22, where it is assumed that $D = 1.1d$; $b = 0.04D_r$. Result: max $D_r = 0.618D$. With regard to the selection of the ratios indicated there, it should be noted that the edge distance of the helicopters is relatively large ($D = 1.1d$). That results in a maximum D_r that is smaller than what could be expected in an actual design. The resulting weights will therefore be conservative, that is, slightly on the high side.

Returning to the performance formula, we can begin

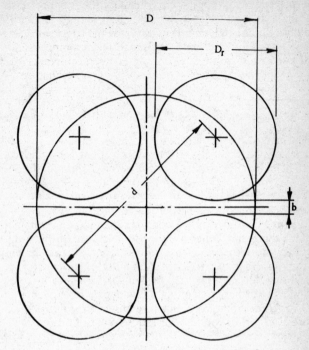

Figure 22 Geometry of the helicopter arrangement

the weight determination. In the technical description
(p. 30) we have established a turbine as the characteristic element. With regard to its weight, such power
plant can neither be compared to a stationary plant, nor
can we use the turbines of our rocket engines, which are
highly sophisticated because of their short service life,
for that purpose. It was only natural, therefore, to derive
the weight from aircraft turbo-engines. Reference 19
contains a long list of existing engines, from which dry
weights as low as about 0.1 kg/hp (0.22 lb/hp) can be
determined. In view of the general uncertainty concerning the actual character of the power plant, the value is
only slightly reduced to 0.09 and 0.075 kg/hp (0.2 and
0.17 lb/hp) for T_1 and T_2, respectively. Due to the in-

ternal composition of such an engine these figures also include at least part of the generator weight. Both the number of the remaining elements for the transformation and transmission of energy, as well as the impossibility of defining them better, prevent us from estimating the weights of any other components. We bypass that problem by assuming that all other parts of the power plant weigh about 1.5 times the turbine weight. That brings the total weight up to 2.5 times the unit weights and we obtain:

$$T_1 \qquad W_4 = 0.0054 \, \frac{W_0}{D_r} \sqrt{W_0}$$

$$T_2 \qquad W_4 = 0.0045 \, \frac{W_0}{D_r} \sqrt{W_0}$$

W_5: Rotor Weight. Current designs would be assessed at about 8–12 percent of the lift-off weight. We will maintain the lower one of these two figures in order to compensate for details that cannot be assessed, and we set for T_1 and T_2

$$W_5 = 0.08 W_0$$

W_6: Landing Gear. Aircraft landing gears weigh about 6–8 percent of the landing weight. In comparison with the landing gears of current heavy aircraft, the landing legs used here are very simple lightweight structures, and their weight percentage is therefore considerably lower. The weight W_6, however, must also include the weight of the wheels. The latter are not used for the landing but only later for a slow rolling on the ground; relatively low weights can therefore be expected for them too. It will be assumed, consequently, that the sum of the weights of both elements is safely covered by the lower of the current weight figures. Since, moreover, the main dimensions of both the footpad of the landing leg as well as the wheel depend on the load-carrying capability of the soil, which is independent of technological developments, we set for T_1 and T_2

$$W_6 = 0.06 W_0$$

W_7: Command Capsule. As we have seen, the capsule is relatively small and practically independent of the dimensions of the spacecraft. Its weight is estimated at 1500 kg. Since this is a very small percentage of the total spacecraft weight, the figure will be kept constant for all spacecraft sizes and for both levels of technology.

3. Results

The calculations that have to be carried out are not difficult although they are somewhat time-consuming. Their results are shown in Fig. 23. The curves marked

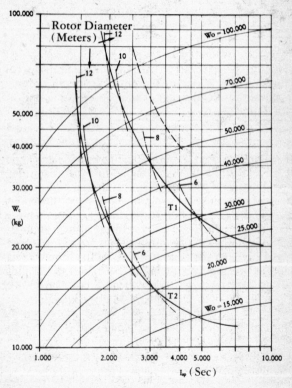

Figure 23   Result of the analysis

W_0 are the result of the first part of our analysis (see p. 160). The curves marked T_1 and T_2 are the final result of the superposition described there. It should be mentioned that in determining weights W_2 and W_3 from Figs. 20 and 21, the amount of thrust was set equal to $1.25W_0$.

Expressing in it general terms, we can say that Fig. 23 shows the weight reductions achievable with increasing specific impulse. The enormous importance of the development of engines with high specific impulse can hardly be demonstrated more impressively. We also see in this figure the very steep weight increase in the low I_{sp} range. It shows us clearly that even the extremely high level of technology, as it is expressed by the T_2 curve, does not make such a vehicle feasible with engines of today's technology, as has already been pointed out (p. 25).

The chart shows short lengths of curves indicating various rotor diameters; the points of intersection of these curves with the main curves (T_1 and T_2) indicate the maximum rotor diameter that is geometrically possible at the respective weights and dimensions. We know from Fig. 22 that the maximum rotor diameter can be about 62% of the diameter of the main body, and we can see now that the latter will vary between about 65 feet and 17 feet over the range investigated here.

Considering the number of assumptions made, it is necessary to determine the sensitivity of the result to possible errors in the weight estimates. The investigation of the impact of a weight increase will be conducted differently in our study than in current actual cases. In the latter we are always working near the upper limits of available I_{sp} values; any weight increase will therefore always result in a performance loss of the vehicle— in whatever form that may be expressed. In our present investigation, however, the I_{sp} value is not really limited. Consequently, an increase of the structural weight does not entail an increase of lift-off weight, because it can be balanced by a reduction of the propellant weight. The reduced amount of propellant, in turn, will be compensated for by an engine with a higher specific impulse.

The dashed line in Fig. 23 shows the result of a 10 percent weight increase for part of the T_1 curve. Such a weight increase can either be shared proportionally by all structural systems or can occur in one group only. We see clearly that even considerable weight corrections will not basically change the results.

In order to find an answer to the question where in the chart we have to look for the spacecraft seen by Ezekiel, it is now only necessary to consider the general relationship of curves T_1 and T_2 to the I_{sp} values. As we have seen, T_1 corresponds to a moderate technical development beyond our own current level, while T_2 postulates a very considerable one. With regard to the specific impulse, its higher values belong quite obviously to a higher level of engine development. It may well be that the level of development is not the same in all fields; in terms of time, such differences between related technologies can only amount to years but certainly not to decades. In order to explain this, let us look at one example: The present high level of the medical sciences is completely unthinkable at the level of electronics and materials sciences of, say, 1940. There are analogous situations in every field. Applied to our graph (Fig. 23), that means generally a connection of low I_{sp} with T_1 and of high I_{sp} with T_2. Graphically illustrated, the actual course of development begins with T_1 and low I_{sp}, and approaches T_2 with progressing development.

Beginning with low I_{sp} values, we find ourselves in the range of relatively large diameters as a result of the above considerations; we find large helicopters and main bodies, and we find the general vehicle characteristics as expressed in Figs. 1 and 2. For an investigation of the other end of the spectrum, we take an I_{sp} value of about 7000 seconds. Even if we assume that the technological development has not completely reached the curve T_2, we find lift-off weights W_0 of 15,000 kg (33,000 lbs) or less. We notice furthermore that the reduction of rotor diameters leads to unrealistic helicopters, and that their power plants assume a disproportionately high percentage of the total weight. A combination of these findings with the fact that the main engine now is not only small, but also is based on a different principle than the one postulated so far, results in the surprising conclusion that the helicopters are not necessary any more. Since the weight of the helicopters and their power plant has become uneconomical, it can now be replaced by respective amounts of propellant, which becomes available for terrestrial flights. Such flights are then time-limited, of course, but that will be acceptable if a propellant is selected that can relatively easily be replenished on earth.

The exchange of the weight of the helicopters and their power plants for propellant weight and volume requires a larger main tank. Fig. 16 shows that such a volume increase can be achieved more economically by an increase of the diameter than by making the "tip" longer. The elimination of the helicopters makes a shortening of the "tip" even *desirable,* with regard to landing properties. In vehicles of that kind we will therefore find a tendency toward a reduction of their relative height. The Langley reports (References 10 to 14) indicate such a possibility. It is quite conceivable, furthermore, that the weight advantage of the concave lower body, which becomes very small in this case, does not justify the increased cost any more, and that the lower part of the vehicle will be given a conical shape.

For the same task, a vehicle of a highly advanced technology will therefore be distinct from one of a lower technology in several important ways:

It will be much smaller.
It will be flatter.
It will not have helicopters.

Fig. 24 shows a comparison of these two extremes.

A comparison of these basic features with Ezekiel's description leaves no doubt that he saw a vehicle of the lower technology; that is, a technology that is only slightly more advanced than our own today. In terms of time we can conclude that only a few decades separate us from that technology.

On the basis of all these considerations we can now locate Ezekiel's spacecraft in the upper left part of the T_1 curve in Fig. 23. We have no way to pinpoint that loca-

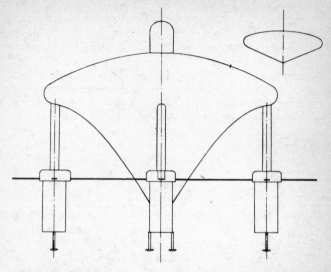

Figure 24 Dependence of vehicle size on development of main power plant

tion exactly; that is insignificant, however, in the context of our search for general order of magnitude. The selection of the point is therefore left to our own judgment, and we locate it at the intersection of T_1 with W_0 = 100,000 kg (220,000 lbs). From that we obtain the other main data of the spaceships:

Specific impulse	I_{sp}	= 2080 sec
Weight of structure	W_0	= 63,300 kg
		(139,000 lbs)
Propellant for return flight	W_9	= 36,700 kg
		(81,000 lbs)
Diameter of main body	D	= 18 m (59.0 ft)
Rotor diameter	D_r	= 11 m (36.1 ft)
Rotor performance (total)	N	= 70,000 hp

The spaceship of Figs. 1 and 4 corresponds to these dimensions.

REFERENCES

A. BIBLES AND BIBLE COMMENTARY

1. *Die Bibel oder die ganze Heilige Schrift des Alten und Neuen Testamentes nach der Ubersetzung von D. Martin Luther*. Stuttgart, no date (supposedly early nineteenth century). Privilegierte Württembergische Bibelanstalt

2. *Biblia. Das ist: die ganze Heilige Schrift*. Translated into German by Dr. Martin Luther. Leipzig, 1842. Mayer und Weigand

3. *The Bible, Revised Standard Version*. New York, © for New Testament 1946, © for Old Testament 1952. American Bible Society

4. *A Catholic Commentary on Holy Scripture*. Toronto, New York, Edinburgh, 1953. Imprimatur 1951. Thomas Nelson & Sons

5. *Die Heilige Schrift des Alten und Neuen Testamentes*. Translated from the original texts and edited by Vinzenz Hamp, Meinard Stenzel, Josef Kürzinger. Aschaffenburg, 1957. Imprimatur 1957. Paul Pattloch

6. *Ezekiel*. Hebrew text and English translation with an introduction and commentary by Rabbi Dr. Fisch, M.A. London, 6th printing 1970. The Soncino Press

7. *The New American Bible*. Translated from the original languages with critical use of all the ancient sources by members of the Catholic Biblical Associa-

tion of America. New York, no date. Imprimatur 1970. P. J. Kenedy & Sons

B. OTHER SOURCES

8. Anderson, Roger A. "Structures Technology—1964." *Astronautics and Aeronautics,* December 1964
9. *Lands of the Bible Today*. Map of the National Geographic Society. Washington, D.C., December 1967
10. Anderson, M. S., et al. "A Tension Shell Structure for Application to Entry Vehicles." *NASA TN D-2675,* March 1965
11. Robinson, J. C., and A. W. Jordan. "Exploratory Experimental Aerodynamic Investigation of Tension Shell Shapes at Mach 7." *NASA TN D-2994,* September 1965
12. Harris, C. D. "Transonic Aerodynamic Investigation of Tension Shell and Blunted 100° Conical Shapes for Unmanned Entry Vehicles." *NASA TN D-3700,* November 1966
13. Sawyer, J. W., and W. D. Deveikis. "Effects of Configuration Modifications on Aerodynamic Characteristics of Tension Shell Shapes at Mach 3.0." *NASA TN D-4080,* August 1967
14. Gibson, F. W. "Aerodynamic Investigation of Some High-Drag Entry Shapes at Mach 15.4." *NASA TN D-4134,* September 1967
15. Blumrich, J. F. "A Rising Tide of Structural Problems." *Astronautics and Aeronautics,* June 1965
16. Blumrich, J. F. "Studies in Advanced Space Vehicle Containers." Advanced Launch Vehicles and Propulsion Systems Conference, Huntsville, Ala., June 1966
17. Bernstein, A. I., and J. F. Blumrich. "Concepts for More Efficient Bulkhead Designs for Launch and Space Vehicles." AIAA/ASME, 9th Structures, Structural Dynamics, and Materials Conference, Palm Springs, Calif., April 1968
18. Just, W. *Einführung in die Aerodynamik und Flugmechanik des Hubschraubers*. Stuttgart, 1957. Verlag Flugtechnik
19. *Aviation Week,* March 13, 1972

INDEX

ABOUT THE AUTHOR

Josef F. Blumrich is chief of the systems layout branch of NASA. Born in Steyr, Austria, in 1913, he came to the United States in 1959, and has worked on spaceship construction matters ever since. He is the holder of many patents and was co-builder of the Saturn V. Blumrich, who received the NASA "Exceptional Service Medal" in 1972, is also the author of many technical articles.

PSYCHIC WORLD

Here are some of the leading books that delve into the world of the occult—that shed light on the powers of prophecy, of reincarnation and of foretelling the future.

OTHER WORLDS.
OTHER REALITIES.

In fact and fiction, these extraordinary books bring the fascinating world of the supernatural down to earth. From ancient astronauts and black magic to witchcraft, voodoo and mysticism—these books look at other worlds and examine other realities.

☐ **POWER THROUGH WITCHCRAFT** (5713/95¢)—Fact

☐ **CHARIOTS OF THE GODS?** (5753/$1.25)—Fact

☐ **A COMPLETE GUIDE TO THE TAROT** (6696/$1.25)—Fact

☐ **WITCHCRAFT AND BLACK MAGIC** (6836/$1.45)—Fact

☐ **THE EXORCIST** (7200/$1.75)—Fiction

☐ **RAGA SIX** (7249/$1.25)—Fiction

☐ **GODS FROM OUTER SPACE** (7276/$1.25)—Fact

☐ **NOT OF THIS WORLD** (7696/$1.25)—Fact

☐ **GOD DRIVES A FLYING SAUCER** (7733/$1.25)—Fact

☐ **LIMBO OF THE LOST** (8243/$1.50)—Fact

FREE!
Bantam Book Catalog

It lists over a thousand money-saving best-sellers originally priced from $3.75 to $15.00 —bestsellers that are yours now for as little as 50¢ to $2.25!

The catalog gives you a great opportunity to build your own private library at huge savings!

So don't delay any longer—send for your catalog TODAY! It's absolutely FREE!